REVISE C1

for MEI Structured Mathematics

Authors
Catherine Berry, Diana Boynova,
Tom Button, Sue de Pomerai

Series Editor
Roger Porkess

HODDER
EDUCATION
AN HACHETTE UK COMPANY

Although every effort has been made to ensure that website addresses are correct at time of going to press, Hodder Education cannot be held responsible for the content of any website mentioned in this book. It is sometimes possible to find a relocated web page by typing in the address of the home page for a website in the URL window of your browser.

Hachette's policy is to use papers that are natural, renewable and recyclable products and made from wood grown in sustainable forests. The logging and manufacturing processes are expected to conform to the environmental regulations of the country of origin.

Orders: please contact Bookpoint Ltd, 130 Milton Park, Abingdon, Oxon OX14 4SB. Telephone: (44) 01235 827720. Fax: (44) 01235 400454. Lines are open 9.00 – 5.00, Monday to Saturday, with a 24-hour message answering service. Visit our website at www.hoddereducation.co.uk

© Catherine Berry, Diana Boynova, Tom Button, Sue de Pomerai, Roger Porkess, 2008
First published in 2008 by
Hodder Education,
An Hachette UK Company
338 Euston Road
London NW1 3BH

Impression number   5   4   3   2
Year   2012   2011   2010

Dynamic Learning Student Online website © Catherine Berry, Diana Boynova, Tom Button, Sue de Pomerai, Roger Porkess, 2008; with contributions from Danielle Veall; developed by Infuze Limited; cast: Tom Frankland, Gina Walker; recorded at Alchemy Soho

Typeset in 11/12 Helvetica by Tech-Set Ltd., Gateshead, Tyne & Wear
Printed in India

A catalogue record for this title is available from the British Library

ISBN: 978 0 340 95733 2

CONTENTS

INTRODUCTION

Welcome to this Revision Guide for the MEI C1 unit!

The book is organised into 19 Sections covering the various topics in the syllabus. They follow essentially the same order as the textbook. A typical Section is four pages long: the first three pages contain essential information and key worked examples covering the topic.

The last page in each Section has questions for you to answer so that you can be sure that you have really understood the topic. There is a multiple-choice exercise and an exam-style question. If you are to gain the greatest possible benefit from the book, and so do your best in the C1 exam, you should work through these for yourself and then refer to the accompanying website to check your answers.

The multiple-choice questions cover the basic ideas and techniques. It is really important that you work through them carefully, guessing will do you no good at all. When you have decided on the answer you think is right, enter it on the website. If you are correct, it tells you so and gives the full solution; check that your answer wasn't just a fluke. If your choice is not right, the website gives you advice about your mistake. The possible wrong answers have all been designed to pick out particular common misunderstandings. The explanations on the website are based on the most likely mistakes. Even if you make a different mistake, you will usually find enough help to set you on the right path so that you can try again.

When you come to the exam-style question, write out your best possible answer. Then go to the website where you will find the solution displayed step-by-step, with someone talking you through it and giving you helpful advice.

So the book both contains the essential information for the exam and, critically, allows you to check that you have understood it properly. That is a recipe for success.

Finally, a word of warning. This book is designed to be used together with the textbook and not as a replacement for it. This Revision Guide will help you to prepare for the exam but to do really well you also need the deep understanding that comes from the detailed explanations you will find in the textbook.

Good learning and good luck!

Catherine Berry, Diana Boynova, Tom Button, Sue de Pomerai, Roger Porkess

Where you see the following icon **DL**, please refer to the Dynamic Learning Student Online website. Information on how to access this website is printed on the inside front cover of this book.

Accompanying books

MEI Structured Mathematics AS Pure Mathematics C1, C2
ISBN 978 0 340 81397 3

Companion to Advanced Mathematics and Statistics
ISBN 978 0 340 95923 7

BASIC ALGEBRA

Expressions and equations

Working with algebraic expressions and solving equations is fundamental to most of the work in AS and A2 Mathematics. In many problems, the work becomes easier if you simplify expressions as you go along. It is important that simplifying expressions becomes second nature to you.

R **REMEMBER**

- Algebra work from GCSE.

K **KEY FACTS**

- Collecting terms means bringing 'like terms' together. You can then add or subtract them.

- Look at the expression $6a + 8b$.
  Both terms in this expression are multiples of 2, so 2 is a factor of both terms.
  This expression can be written as $2(3a + 4b)$. This process is called factorising.

- The reverse of factorising is multiplying out brackets. You can multiply out the brackets for the expression $2(3a + 4b)$ by multiplying both terms in the bracket by 2, giving $6a + 8b$. This can also be called 'expanding' or 'opening' the brackets.

- When you are solving an equation, remember that you must always carry out the same operation on both sides of the equation.

Collecting terms

An expression can sometimes be simplified by collecting 'like terms'.
Like terms are terms which involve exactly the same variables. So $2x^2$ and $-3x^2$ are like terms. $2x^2 - 3x^2$ can be simplified to $-x^2$, but $5a$ and $3ab$ are unlike terms, and so $5a + 3ab$ cannot be simplified.

EXAMPLE 1	Simplify $2a + 3b - 4 + 5a + 1$.

There are two terms in a: $2a$ and $5a$, which can be added. There are also two constant terms: -4 and 1, which can be added.

SOLUTION	$2a + 3b - 4 + 5a + 1 = (2a + 5a) + 3b + (-4 + 1)$ $= 7a + 3b - 3$

Multiplying out brackets

Each term in the bracket must be multiplied by the term outside the bracket.

EXAMPLE 2	Multiply out and simplify the expression $3(2x - 4) + 5(1 - x)$.

SOLUTION	

$$3(2x - 4) + 5(1 - x)$$

Multiply out the brackets $\qquad = 6x - 12 + 5 - 5x$
Collect together like terms and simplify $\quad = x - 7$

EXAMPLE 3

Multiply out and simplify the expression $2x(x - 3y) - y(2x - 3)$.

SOLUTION

$$2x(x - 3y) - y(2x - 3)$$
Multiply out the brackets $= 2x^2 - 6xy - 2xy + 3y$
Collect together like terms $= 2x^2 - 8xy + 3y$

Be careful with signs.

When two brackets are involved, each term in the first bracket must be multiplied by each term in the second bracket.

EXAMPLE 4

Multiply out the expression $(a - 3)(2b - 1)$.

This means $(a - 3) \times (2b - 1)$.

SOLUTION

$$(a - 3) \times (2b - 1) = (a \times 2b) + (a \times -1) + (-3 \times 2b) + (-3 \times -1)$$
$$= 2ab - a - 6b + 3$$

EXAMPLE 5

Multiply out and simplify $(2x - 1)(3x + 4)$.

SOLUTION

Multiply out $\quad (2x - 1)(3x + 4) = 6x^2 + 8x - 3x - 4$
Simplify $\qquad\qquad\qquad\qquad = 6x^2 + 5x - 4$

Factorising

Factorising an expression means writing the expression as the product of two or more factors. These factors may be numbers, letters or a combination of letters and numbers. You need to look for numbers or letters which are factors of each term in the expression.

A ADVICE

You can check factorising by multiplying out the brackets.

EXAMPLE 6

Factorise $12x + 20y - 4$.

SOLUTION

$$12x + 20y - 4 = 4(3x + 5y - 1)$$

The largest number which is a factor of 12, 20 and 4 is 4, so you can take out a factor of 4. This means that you need to divide each term by 4.

EXAMPLE 7

Factorise $2p^2 - 3pq$.

SOLUTION

$$2p^2 - 3pq = p(2p - 3q)$$

p is a factor of both terms, so you can take out a factor p. This means that you need to divide both terms by p.

Remember that $2p^2 \div p$ is $2p$.

Sometimes both letters and numbers are factors. You need to make sure that you have taken out all possible factors.

| EXAMPLE 8 | Factorise $6a^2b + 12a^2b^3 + 4a^3b^2$. |

| SOLUTION | $6a^2b + 12a^2b^3 + 4a^3b^2 = 2a^2b(3 + 6b^2 + 2ab)$ |

The largest number which is a factor of 6, 12 and 4 is 2, so you can take out a factor of 2. You can also take out a factor a^2, and a factor b. So the factor you are taking out is $2a^2b$. You need to divide each term by $2a^2b$.

⚠ We often talk about 'taking out a factor'. This suggests that subtraction is involved, but this is not the case. When you take out a factor, you are in fact dividing each term by that factor.

Equations

To solve an equation, you must carry out the same operation on both sides of the equation.

| EXAMPLE 9 | Solve the equation $5x - 4 = 3$. |

| SOLUTION | |

Add 4 to both sides

$$5x - 4 + 4 = 3 + 4$$
$$5x = 7$$

Divide both sides by 5

$$\frac{5x}{5} = \frac{7}{5}$$

$$x = \frac{7}{5}$$

You can miss out these lines when you feel confident.

⚠ Make sure that you understand the difference between an equation, an identity and an expression. Equations and identities involve an 'equals' sign, but expressions do not.
An identity is true for all values of the variable, but an equation is true for just some — the solutions of the equation.

For example, $5x + 2$ is an expression
$5x + 2 = 12$ is an equation
$5x + 2 = x + 2(2x + 1)$ is an identity.

This is true for only one value of x. It is true when $x = 2$.

This is true for all values of x.

In equations where the variable appears on both sides of the equation, you need to collect terms involving the variable on one side and constant terms on the other.

| EXAMPLE 10 | Solve the equation $3x + 6 = x - 4$. |

| SOLUTION | |

Subtract x from both sides

$$3x - x + 6 = -4$$
$$2x + 6 = -4$$

Subtract 6 from both sides

$$2x = -4 - 6$$
$$2x = -10$$

Divide both sides by 2

$$x = -5$$

Sometimes you may need to multiply out brackets before solving the equation.

EXAMPLE 11

Solve the equation $3(2x - 1) + 4 = 1 - 2(x + 3)$.

SOLUTION

Multiply out the brackets	$6x - 3 + 4 = 1 - 2x - 6$
Simplify	$6x + 1 = -5 - 2x$
Add $2x$ to both sides	$6x + 1 + 2x = -5$
	$8x + 1 = -5$
Subtract 1 from both sides	$8x = -6$
Divide both sides by 8	$x = -\frac{6}{8}$
	$x = -\frac{3}{4}$

LINKS

You may meet this work in any other units at this level.

Test Yourself ⊃L

1 Solve the equation $5 - 2x = x + 4$.

A $x = \frac{1}{3}$ **B** $x = 3$ **C** $x = -1$ **D** $x = -3$ **E** $x = -9$

2 Solve the equation $3(x - 2) = 4 - (2x + 1)$.

A $x = \frac{11}{5}$ **B** $x = 9$ **C** $x = -\frac{3}{5}$ **D** $x = 1$ **E** $x = \frac{9}{5}$

3 Multiply out and simplify $(2x + 5)(3x - 2)$.

A $5x^2 + 11x - 10$ **B** $5x^2 + 19x - 10$ **C** $6x^2 + 11x - 10$

D $6x^2 + 19x - 10$ **E** $6x^2 - 10$

4 Simplify $3x(2x - y) - (x - 1)(2x + 3)$ as far as possible.

A $6x^2 - 3xy - 2x^2 - x + 3$ **B** $4x^2 - 3xy - x - 3$ **C** $4x^2 - 3xy - x + 3$

D $3x^2 - 3xy - x + 3$ **E** $4x^2 - 3xy + x - 3$

5 Factorise $4a^2b^3c + 12ab^2c^2 - 4ab^2$ as far as possible.

A $4ab^2(abc + 3c^2)$ **B** $4ab^2(abc + 8c^2)$ **C** $ab^2(4abc + 12c^2 - 4)$

D $4ab^2(abc + 3c^2 - 1)$ **E** $4ab(ab^2c + 3bc^2 - b)$

Exam-Style Question ⊃L

i) Simplify $(x^2 + 2)^2 - (x^2 - 2)^2$ as far as possible.

ii) Hence solve the equation $(x^2 + 2)^2 - (x^2 - 2)^2 = 8x^2 - 4x + 12$.

Working with fractions and powers

A ABOUT THIS TOPIC

In your AS and A2 Mathematics work you will often have to work with algebraic expressions involving fractions or powers. It is important that you are confident in manipulating these expressions.

R REMEMBER

- Work on numerical fractions from GCSE.
- Algebra work from GCSE and C1, in particular multiplying out brackets.

K KEY FACTS

- Look at the fraction $\dfrac{3x + 6}{4x + 8}$.

  > The top line is the numerator.
  >
  > The bottom line is the denominator.

  You can factorise both the numerator and the denominator: $\dfrac{3(x + 2)}{4(x + 2)}$.

  There is a common factor, $x + 2$, so you can cancel to get $\dfrac{3}{4}$.

- The same rules apply to adding, subtracting, multiplying and dividing algebraic fractions as for numerical ones.

- To solve an equation with fractions, such as $\dfrac{x}{2} + \dfrac{3x + 5}{5} = 12$, start by multiplying each term by the same number or expression to clear the fractions; in this case 10 is a suitable number.

Multiplying expressions

When multiplying terms involving letters and numbers, you multiply the numbers together and combine the letters by thinking about how many times each letter is being multiplied.

 In problems like that in Example 1, notice that the coefficient of the final answer is obtained by multiplying 2, 3 and 5. A common mistake is to treat this expression as if you were multiplying out brackets, and multiply both the 3 and the 5 by 2, giving 60 instead of 30.

EXAMPLE 1

Simplify $2x^2yz \times 3z^2 \times 5xy^3$.

SOLUTION

$$2x^2yz \times 3z^2 \times 5xy^3 = 2 \times 3 \times 5 \times x^2 \times x \times y \times y^3 \times z \times z^2$$
$$= 30 \times x^3 \times y^4 \times z^3$$
$$= 30x^3y^4z^3$$

Simplifying fractions

Sometimes you may need to simplify algebraic fractions. You can simplify a fraction if both the numerator and the denominator have a common factor. In that case you can cancel.

EXAMPLE 2 Simplify $\dfrac{3a^2bc}{12ac^3}$.

The common factors of the top and bottom line are 3, a and c.

SOLUTION

$$\dfrac{\cancel{3}\,a^{\cancel{2}}b\,\cancel{c}}{\cancel{4}\,\cancel{12}\,\cancel{a}c^{\cancel{3}\,2}} = \dfrac{ab}{4c^2}$$

Sometimes you may need to factorise to identify common factors before you can cancel.

EXAMPLE 3 Simplify $\dfrac{2pq^2 + pq}{4q^2 + 2q}$.

The common factors are q and $(2q + 1)$.

SOLUTION

$$\dfrac{2pq^2 + pq}{4q^2 + 2q} = \dfrac{p\,\cancel{q}\,\cancel{(2q + 1)}}{2\,\cancel{q}\,\cancel{(2q + 1)}}$$

$$= \dfrac{p}{2}$$

Multiplying and dividing fractions

You multiply algebraic fractions in the same way that you multiply numerical fractions: by multiplying their top lines and multiplying their bottom lines. You should always simplify if possible. It is usually easier to cancel where possible before doing the multiplying.

We often talk about 'cancelling' fractions. Remember that when you are cancelling a fraction, you are dividing each of the top and bottom lines by the same factor. You can only cancel if they have a common factor. So, for example, you cannot cancel the x's in the fraction $\dfrac{x + 2}{x}$, since x is not a factor of the top line.

EXAMPLE 4 Simplify $\dfrac{2a^2}{3b^4} \times \dfrac{6b^2c}{a}$.

You can cancel factors of 3, a and b^2.

SOLUTION

$$\dfrac{2a^{\cancel{2}}}{\cancel{3}b^{\cancel{4}\,2}} \times \dfrac{\cancel{2}\,\cancel{6}b^{\cancel{2}}c}{\cancel{a}} = \dfrac{2a}{b^2} \times \dfrac{2c}{1}$$

$$= \dfrac{4ac}{b^2}$$

You divide algebraic fractions in the same way as you divide numerical fractions. Dividing by a fraction is equivalent to multiplying by the reciprocal of the fraction.

EXAMPLE 5 Simplify $\dfrac{p^2 + pq}{2q} \div \dfrac{p}{4q^2}$.

SOLUTION

$$\dfrac{p^2 + pq}{2q} \div \dfrac{p}{4q^2} = \dfrac{p^2 + pq}{2q} \times \dfrac{4q^2}{p}$$

Turn the second fraction 'upside-down' to give the reciprocal.

$$= \dfrac{\cancel{p}\,(p + q)}{\cancel{2}\,\cancel{q}} \times \dfrac{2\,\cancel{4}\,q^{\cancel{2}}}{\cancel{p}}$$

You can cancel the factors 2, p and q.

$$= 2q(p + q)$$

Adding and subtracting fractions

When you add or subtract algebraic fractions, you need to find a common denominator, just as you do for numerical fractions.

EXAMPLE 6

Simplify $\dfrac{1-a}{2a} - \dfrac{2b+3}{3b}$.

SOLUTION

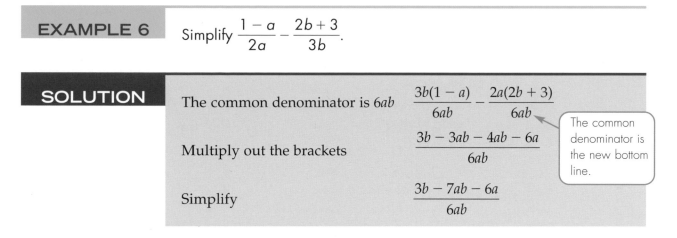

The common denominator is $6ab$ $\dfrac{3b(1-a)}{6ab} - \dfrac{2a(2b+3)}{6ab}$

> The common denominator is the new bottom line.

Multiply out the brackets $\dfrac{3b - 3ab - 4ab - 6a}{6ab}$

Simplify $\dfrac{3b - 7ab - 6a}{6ab}$

Solving equations involving fractions

In equations involving fractions, it is best to multiply through to clear the fractions at the start. Remember that you may need to use brackets.

EXAMPLE 7

Solve the equation $\dfrac{x-2}{3} = \dfrac{2x+1}{2} - 4$.

SOLUTION

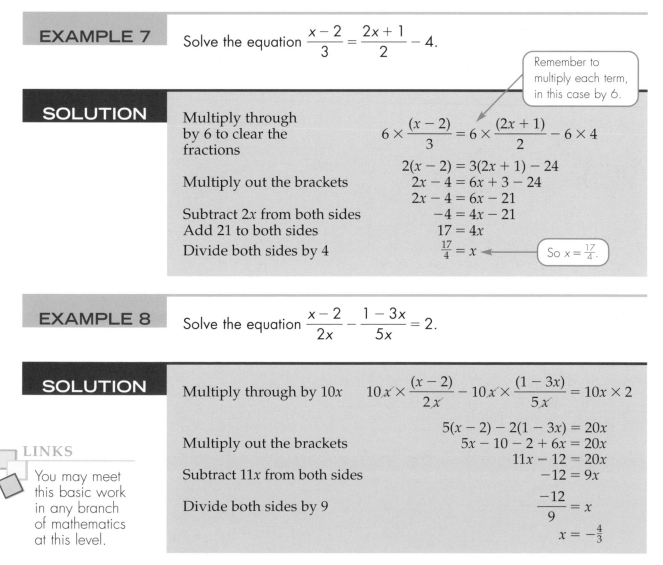

> Remember to multiply each term, in this case by 6.

Multiply through by 6 to clear the fractions

$$6 \times \frac{(x-2)}{3} = 6 \times \frac{(2x+1)}{2} - 6 \times 4$$

Multiply out the brackets

$$2(x-2) = 3(2x+1) - 24$$
$$2x - 4 = 6x + 3 - 24$$
$$2x - 4 = 6x - 21$$

Subtract $2x$ from both sides

$$-4 = 4x - 21$$

Add 21 to both sides

$$17 = 4x$$

Divide both sides by 4

$$\frac{17}{4} = x$$

> So $x = \frac{17}{4}$.

EXAMPLE 8

Solve the equation $\dfrac{x-2}{2x} - \dfrac{1-3x}{5x} = 2$.

SOLUTION

Multiply through by $10x$ $10x \times \dfrac{(x-2)}{2x} - 10x \times \dfrac{(1-3x)}{5x} = 10x \times 2$

$$5(x-2) - 2(1-3x) = 20x$$

Multiply out the brackets

$$5x - 10 - 2 + 6x = 20x$$
$$11x - 12 = 20x$$

Subtract $11x$ from both sides

$$-12 = 9x$$

Divide both sides by 9

$$\frac{-12}{9} = x$$

$$x = -\frac{4}{3}$$

LINKS

You may meet this basic work in any branch of mathematics at this level.

Test Yourself ▷L

1 Simplify $4x^2y^3 \times 2xz^4 \times 3y^2$ as far as possible.

   A $24x^3y^5z^4$ **B** $48x^3y^5z^4$ **C** $9x^3y^5z^4$

   D $24x^3y^6z^4$ **E** $48x^3y^6z^4$

2 Simplify $\dfrac{12p^2q^6r}{8pq^2r^3}$ as far as possible.

   A $\dfrac{4pq^4}{r^2}$ **B** $\dfrac{12pq^3}{8r^2}$ **C** $\dfrac{3pq^3}{2r^2}$

   D $\dfrac{3pq^4}{2r^2}$ **E** $\dfrac{4pq^3}{r^2}$

3 Write $\dfrac{2x+1}{3y} + \dfrac{1-x}{2y}$ as a single fraction.

   A $\dfrac{x+2}{5y}$ **B** $\dfrac{x+5}{6y}$ **C** $\dfrac{x+5}{5y}$

   D $\dfrac{x+2}{6y}$ **E** $\dfrac{3x+4}{6y}$

4 Simplify $\dfrac{6x^3}{(x+1)^2} \times \dfrac{3x+3}{2x}$ as far as possible.

   A $9x$ **B** $\dfrac{6x^3(x+3)}{(x+1)^2}$ **C** $\dfrac{3x^2(3x+3)}{(x+1)^2}$

   D $\dfrac{12x^2}{x+1}$ **E** $\dfrac{9x^2}{x+1}$

5 Solve the equation $\dfrac{3}{2x} + \dfrac{1-x}{x} = 2$.

   A $x = \frac{5}{6}$ **B** $x = \frac{3}{2}$ **C** $x = \frac{4}{7}$ **D** $x = \frac{4}{5}$ **E** $x = 1$

Exam-Style Question ▷L

a) Simplify the expression $2p^2q \times (3pq)^2$ as far as possible.

b) Write $\dfrac{3}{2x} - \dfrac{2}{x^2}$ as a single fraction.

Change of subject

A ABOUT THIS TOPIC

Changing the subject of a formula is an important skill which is needed in many areas of mathematics.

R REMEMBER

- Solving linear equations from GCSE and C1.

K KEY FACTS

- You can rearrange a formula in the same way that you solve an equation, but using letters instead of numbers.

Changing the subject of a formula

When you change the subject of a formula, you should think of it as solving an equation. Whatever you do to one side of the formula, you must do to the other.

EXAMPLE 1

Make x the subject of the formula $\dfrac{ax}{b} = c$.

SOLUTION

Multiply both sides by b $ax = bc$

Divide both sides by a $x = \dfrac{bc}{a}$

A ADVICE

It is important to make sure that you carry out the steps in the right order. Suppose the new subject of the formula is to be x. Think about what is being done to x, in what order, in the formula. You need to undo these steps in reverse order.

EXAMPLE 2

Make x the subject of the formula $px - q = r$.

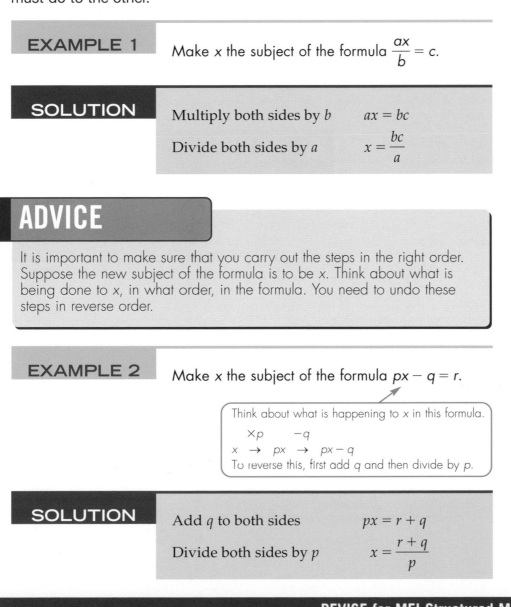

Think about what is happening to x in this formula.

$$x \xrightarrow{\times p} px \xrightarrow{-q} px - q$$

To reverse this, first add q and then divide by p.

SOLUTION

Add q to both sides $px = r + q$

Divide both sides by p $x = \dfrac{r + q}{p}$

EXAMPLE 3   Make x the subject of the formula $\frac{1}{2}a(x + b) = d$.

Think about what is happening to x in this formula.

$$\begin{array}{ccccccc} & +b & & \times a & & \div 2 & \\ x & \to & x + b & \to & a(x + b) & \to & \frac{1}{2}a(x + b) \end{array}$$

To reverse this, first multiply by 2 and divide by a, then subtract b.

SOLUTION

Multiply both sides by 2	$a(x + b) = 2d$
Divide both sides by a	$x + b = \dfrac{2d}{a}$
Subtract b from both sides	$x = \dfrac{2d}{a} - b$

EXAMPLE 4   Make v the subject of the formula $2v^2 + u = w$.

SOLUTION

Subtract u from both sides	$2v^2 = w - u$
Divide both sides by 2	$v^2 = \dfrac{w - u}{2}$
Square root both sides	$v = \sqrt{\dfrac{w - u}{2}}$

On the left-hand side of this formula, first you square v, then multiply by 2, then add u. So you need to subtract u first, then divide by 2, and finally take the square root.

⚠ In the example above, it is important to make sure that the square root sign covers the whole fraction, including the bottom line, to show that you are taking the square root of the whole fraction rather than just part of it.

A ADVICE

The new subject of the equation needs to be positive. If the term containing the new term is negative, it is best to add this term to both sides first.

EXAMPLE 5   Make y the subject of the formula $a - by = c$.

SOLUTION

Add by to each side	$a = c + by$
Subtract c from each side	$a - c = by$
Divide both sides by b	$\dfrac{a - c}{b} = y$
	$y = \dfrac{a - c}{b}$

If the new subject is in the bottom line (the denominator) of a fraction, you will need to multiply through by that denominator to clear the fractions.

EXAMPLE 6

Make x the subject of the formula $\dfrac{k}{x-m} = n$.

SOLUTION

Multiply both sides by $x - m$ $k = n(x - m)$

Divide both sides by n $\dfrac{k}{n} = x - m$

Add m to both sides $\dfrac{k}{n} + m = x$

$$x = \dfrac{k}{n} + m$$

> Remember to use brackets where necessary.

EXAMPLE 7

Make p the subject of the formula $r - \dfrac{q}{p} = s$.

SOLUTION

Add $\dfrac{q}{p}$ to both sides $r = s + \dfrac{q}{p}$

Subtract s from both sides $r - s = \dfrac{q}{p}$

Multiply both sides by p $p(r - s) = q$

Divide both sides by $(r - s)$ $p = \dfrac{q}{r - s}$

EXAMPLE 8

Make x the subject of the formula $\dfrac{k}{\sqrt{a^2 - x^2}} = b$.

SOLUTION

Multiply both sides by $\sqrt{a^2 - x^2}$ $k = b\sqrt{a^2 - x^2}$

Divide both sides by b $\dfrac{k}{b} = \sqrt{a^2 - x^2}$

Square both sides $\dfrac{k^2}{b^2} = a^2 - x^2$

Add x^2 to both sides $\dfrac{k^2}{b^2} + x^2 = a^2$

Subtract $\dfrac{k^2}{b^2}$ from both sides $x^2 = a^2 - \dfrac{k^2}{b^2}$

Square root both sides $x = \sqrt{a^2 - \dfrac{k^2}{b^2}}$

> The term in x is in the denominator of the fraction, so multiply both sides by the whole denominator.

> The term in x is negative, so add this term to both sides.

If the new subject appears in more than one term, these terms need to be collected together and factorised.

EXAMPLE 9   Make y the subject of the equation $py + q = a - by$.

SOLUTION

Add by to both sides	$py + q + by = a$
Subtract q from both sides	$py + by = a - q$
Factorise the left-hand side	$y(p + b) = a - q$
Divide both sides by $p + b$	$y = \dfrac{a - q}{p + b}$

> Collect the terms in y on the left, and the other terms on the right.

EXAMPLE 10   Make a the subject of the formula $\dfrac{3a - b}{2a + 1} = 2b$.

SOLUTION

Multiply both sides by $2a + 1$	$3a - b = 2b(2a + 1)$
Multiply out the brackets	$3a - b = 4ab + 2b$
Add b to both sides	$3a = 4ab + 3b$
Subtract $4ab$ from both sides	$3a - 4ab = 3b$
Factorise the left-hand side	$a(3 - 4b) = 3b$
Divide both sides by $3 - 4b$	$a = \dfrac{3b}{3 - 4b}$

> There is a term in a in the denominator, so multiply both sides by this denominator.

> Collect the terms in a on the left, and the other terms on the right.

🔲 LINKS

You will meet this work throughout mathematics, including other units at any level.

Test Yourself ▶L

1 Make x the subject of the formula $\dfrac{ax + b}{c} = d$.

A $x = \dfrac{cd}{a} - b$ **B** $x = \dfrac{c(d - b)}{a}$ **C** $x = cd - b - a$

D $x = \dfrac{cd - b}{a}$ **E** $x = \dfrac{cd}{a} - b$

2 Make y the subject of the formula $p\sqrt{y - r} = q$.

A $y = \dfrac{q^2}{p^2} + r$ **B** $y = \dfrac{q^2}{p} + r$ **C** $y = \left(\dfrac{q}{p} + r\right)^2$

D $y = \left(\dfrac{q + r}{p}\right)^2$ **E** $y = \dfrac{q^2 + r}{p}$

3 Make p the subject of the formula $x - \dfrac{p}{y} = z$.

A $p = y(z - x)$ **B** $p = y(x + z)$ **C** $p = x - yz$

D $p = y(x - z)$ **E** $p = xy - z$

4 Make x the subject of the formula $\dfrac{a}{x^2 + b} = c$.

A $x = \sqrt{\dfrac{a}{c} - b}$

B $x = \sqrt{\dfrac{c}{a} - b}$

C $x = \sqrt{\dfrac{a}{c}} - b$

D $x = \sqrt{\dfrac{a - b}{c}}$

E $x = \dfrac{\sqrt{a}}{\sqrt{c}} - \sqrt{b}$

5 Make x the subject of the formula $\dfrac{x}{a} = b - x$.

A $x = \dfrac{ab}{2}$

B $x = a(b - x)$

C $x = b - \dfrac{x}{a}$

D $x = \dfrac{b}{2}$

E $x = \dfrac{ab}{1 + a}$

Exam-Style Question ▶L

i) Make r the subject of the formula $P = \frac{2}{3}Mr^2$.

ii) Make x the subject of the formula $c = \dfrac{ax + c}{x - 2}$.

Quadratic equations

K **KEY FACTS**

- Some quadratic equations can be solved by factorising.
- The quadratic formula for solutions of the equation $ax^2 + bx + c = 0$ is

$$x = \frac{-b \pm \sqrt{b^2 - 4ac}}{2a}.$$

- The discriminant of the above quadratic equation is given by $b^2 - 4ac$. The sign of the discriminant tells you how many real roots to expect.

Discriminant	Positive	Zero	Negative
Number of real roots	2	1 (repeated)	0

Quadratic factorising

The procedure for factorising a quadratic expression is shown in the two examples below.

x^2 means $1x^2$
$1 \times -21 = -21$

EXAMPLE 1   Factorise $x^2 + 4x - 21$.

SOLUTION

The product of the two outside numbers is -21.
Look for two numbers which multiply to give -21 and add to give 4.
These numbers are 7 and -3.
Split the middle term using
these numbers $x^2 + 4x - 21 = x^2 + 7x - 3x - 21$
Factorise in pairs $= x(x + 7) - 3(x + 7)$
The two terms have a common factor of $x + 7$ $= (x + 7)(x - 3)$

EXAMPLE 2   Factorise $3x^2 - 20x + 12$.

$3 \times 12 = 36$

SOLUTION

The product of the two outside numbers is 36.
Look for two numbers which multiply to give 36 and add to give -20.
These numbers are -2 and -18.
Split the middle term $3x^2 - 20x + 12 = 3x^2 - 2x - 18x + 12$
Factorise in pairs $= x(3x - 2) - 6(3x - 2)$
There is now a common factor of $3x - 2$ $= (x - 6)(3x - 2)$

Solving quadratic equations by factorising

A quadratic equation can be written in the form $ax^2 + bx + c = 0$.
Some quadratic equations can be solved by factorising the expression
on the left-hand side.

EXAMPLE 3

Solve the equation $2x^2 - 5x - 12 = 0$.

SOLUTION

Factorising the left-hand side

$$2x^2 - 5x - 12 = 0$$
$$2x^2 - 8x + 3x - 12 = 0$$
$$2x(x - 4) + 3(x - 4) = 0$$
$$(2x + 3)(x - 4) = 0$$

Either $2x + 3 = 0$ or $x - 4 = 0$
The solution is $x = -\frac{3}{2}$ or $x = 4$.

> Since the product of the two factors is zero, one or other of them must equal zero, giving two roots for the equation.

Quadratic equations which cannot be factorised

Not all quadratic equations can be factorised. There are other methods
for solving quadratic equations which cannot be factorised.

- You can plot the graph of the quadratic function and find the points at
  which the graph cuts the x axis. However, this does not give a
  completely accurate answer.
- The method of completing the square can be used.
- The quadratic formula can be used. This is the usual method for
  solving a quadratic equation which cannot be factorised. It is a
  generalisation of the method of completing the square.
  The quadratic formula giving the solution of the quadratic equation
  $ax^2 + bx + c = 0$ is

$$x = \frac{-b \pm \sqrt{b^2 - 4ac}}{2a}.$$

EXAMPLE 4

Solve the equation $2x^2 + x - 4 = 0$, giving your answers in exact form.

SOLUTION

In this case $a = 2$, $b = 1$ and $c = -4$.

Using the quadratic formula $\quad x = \dfrac{-1 \pm \sqrt{1^2 - 4 \times 2 \times -4}}{2 \times 2}$

$$= \frac{-1 \pm \sqrt{33}}{4}$$

> The C1 examination is a non-calculator paper, so you will be asked to leave answers like this one in square root form. This is the exact form.

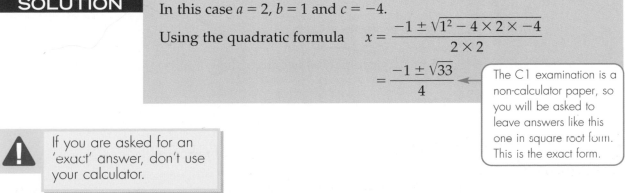

! If you are asked for an 'exact' answer, don't use your calculator.

The discriminant of a quadratic equation

In the quadratic formula, the part of the equation under the square root sign is called the discriminant.

The discriminant of the quadratic equation $ax^2 + bx + c = 0$ is $b^2 - 4ac$.

The value of the discriminant is important as it tells you whether or not there are real roots to the equation.

- If the discriminant is positive, the equation has two real roots.
- If the discriminant is negative, the equation has no real roots.
- If the discriminant is zero, then the equation has one repeated root.

The number of roots corresponds to the number of times the graph of the quadratic function meets the x axis.

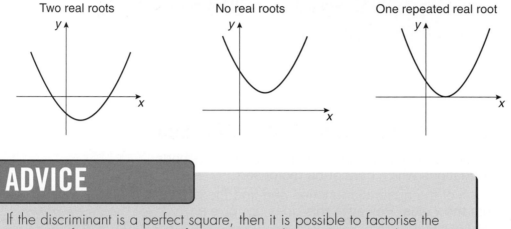

Two real roots   No real roots   One repeated real root

A ADVICE

If the discriminant is a perfect square, then it is possible to factorise the equation. If you are trying to factorise a quadratic equation and are not sure if it is possible to do so, then working out the discriminant tells you whether you should persevere with factorising, or use the formula instead.

EXAMPLE 5

Find the discriminant of the quadratic equation $2x^2 - 3x + 5 = 0$. State the number of real roots of this equation.

SOLUTION

For the quadratic equation $2x^2 - 3x + 5 = 0$

$$a = 2, b = -3, c = 5$$

Discriminant $= b^2 - 4ac$
$$= (-3)^2 - 4 \times 2 \times 5$$
$$= 9 - 40$$
$$= -31$$

Since the discriminant is negative, the equation has no real roots.

LINKS

Pure Mathematics	Polynomials (C1).
	May be required in a wide variety of topics.
Mechanics	Projectiles (M1).
	May be required in other topics.

Test Yourself ⅅ

1 Which of the following is the solution of the quadratic equation $x^2 - 5x - 6 = 0$?

   A $x = -6$ or $x = 1$ **B** $x = -2$ or $x = 3$ **C** $x = 2$ or $x = 3$

   D $x = -3$ or $x = 2$ **E** $x = -1$ or $x = 6$

2 Which of the following is the solution of the quadratic equation $2x^2 - 9x - 18 = 0$?

   A $x = \frac{3}{2}$ or $x = -6$ **B** $x = \frac{9}{2}$ or $x = -2$ **C** $x = 6$ or $x = 3$

   D $x = -\frac{9}{2}$ or $x = 2$ **E** $x = -\frac{3}{2}$ or $x = 6$

3 Which of the following is the solution of the quadratic equation $2x^2 - 3x - 4 = 0$?

   A $x = \dfrac{-3 \pm \sqrt{41}}{4}$ **B** $x = \dfrac{3 \pm \sqrt{41}}{4}$ **C** $x = \dfrac{3 \pm \sqrt{23}}{4}$

   D $x = \dfrac{-3 \pm \sqrt{23}}{4}$ **E** There are no real roots

4 Simplify the expression $\dfrac{x^2 - 9}{x^2 - x - 12}$ as far as possible.

   A $\dfrac{9}{x - 12}$ **B** $\dfrac{3}{4}$ **C** $\dfrac{x + 3}{x - 4}$

   D $\dfrac{x - 3}{x - 4}$ **E** $\dfrac{x + 3}{x + 4}$

5 Four of the following statements are true and one is false. Which one is false?

   A $3x^2 - 2x + 1 = 0$ has no real roots.

   B $2x^2 - 5x + 1 = 0$ has two distinct real roots.

   C $9x^2 - 6x + 1 = 0$ has one repeated real root.

   D $x^2 + 2x - 5 = 0$ has two distinct real roots.

   E $4x^2 - 9 = 0$ has one repeated real root.

Exam-Style Question ⅅ

i)   Find the value of k for which the equation $4x^2 - 12x + k = 0$ has exactly one real root.

ii)   Solve the equation $4x^2 - 12x + 9 = 0$.

Simultaneous equations

You may need to solve simultaneous equations in many areas of mathematics. You have solved linear simultaneous equations at GCSE level; in C1 you revise this and extend the work to include solving one linear and one quadratic equation.

- Solving linear simultaneous equations from GCSE.
- Solving quadratic equations from C1.

- Linear simultaneous equations can be solved by either the method of elimination or the method of substitution.

- One linear and one quadratic equation are usually best solved by substituting the linear equation into the quadratic equation.

Linear simultaneous equations

A linear equation is an equation whose graph is a straight line. Examples of linear equations are $2x - 3y = 1$ and $y = 3 - 4x$. Linear equations do not involve terms in any powers of x or y, for example x^2 or y^2, or terms such as xy.

If you draw the graphs of two linear equations, then unless the graphs are parallel, they must intersect at some point (and only at one point). The co-ordinates of the point of intersection give the solution to the two linear simultaneous equations.

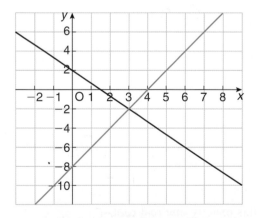

This diagram shows the graphs of $2x - y = 8$ and $4x + 3y = 6$. The graphs intersect at the point $(3, -2)$, so the solution of the two linear simultaneous equations is $x = 3, y = -2$. Check that these values satisfy both the equations.

Drawing graphs to find the solution of two simultaneous linear equations may not give an exact solution. You will usually be expected to solve equations like these algebraically. There are two different methods: the elimination method and the substitution method.

Linear simultaneous equations: elimination method

In the elimination method, you multiply one or both of the equations through by a constant, so that adding or subtracting the resulting equations eliminates one of the unknowns.

A ADVICE

Check your answers by substituting into both the original equations. It is very common to make errors with signs.

EXAMPLE 1

Solve the simultaneous equations

$$2x - y = 8 \quad ①$$
$$4x + 3y = 6 \quad ②$$

SOLUTION

Multiply equation ① by 3 $6x - 3y = 24$
Leave equation ② as it is $4x + 3y = 6$

Add the equations $10x = 30 \Rightarrow x = 3$
Substitute $x = 3$ into equation ① $6 - y = 8 \Rightarrow y = -2$
The solution is $x = 3$, $y = -2$.

EXAMPLE 2

Solve the simultaneous equations

$$2x - 5y = 5 \quad ①$$
$$3x - 2y = 13 \quad ②$$

> Alternatively, you could eliminate the y's by multiplying the first equation by 2 and the second by 5.

SOLUTION

Multiply equation ① by 3 $6x - 15y = 15$
Multiply equation ② by 2 $6x - 4y = 26$

Subtract the equations $-11y = -11 \Rightarrow y = 1$
Substitute $y = 1$ into equation ① $2x - 5 = 5 \Rightarrow x = 5$
The solution is $x = 5$, $y = 1$.

Linear simultaneous equations: substitution method

The substitution method is particularly useful if one equation gives one variable in terms of the other, or can easily be rewritten in this form.

EXAMPLE 3

Solve the simultaneous equations

$$3x - 4y = 2 \quad ①$$
$$y = 2x + 1 \quad ②$$

> Replace 'y' in the first equation by '$2x + 1$'.

SOLUTION

Substitute equation ② into equation ① $3x - 4(2x + 1) = 2$
$$3x - 8x - 4 = 2$$
$$-5x = 6$$
$$x = -1.2$$

Substitute $x = -1.2$ into equation ② $y = -2.4 + 1 = -1.4$
The solution is $x = -1.2$, $y = -1.4$.

Non-linear simultaneous equations

Non-linear equations might involve terms such as x^2, y^2 or other powers. The graph of a non-linear equation is not a straight line. As with linear simultaneous equations, you can find an approximate solution by plotting the graphs of both equations and finding the point(s) of intersection. There may be one, more than one, or none at all!

Some non-linear simultaneous equations cannot be solved algebraically. However, in the case when one equation is linear and the other is quadratic, the substitution method can be used.

One linear and one quadratic equation: substitution method

Rearrange the linear equation if necessary so that one variable is given in terms of the other, and then substitute this into the quadratic equation.

EXAMPLE 4

Solve the simultaneous equations

$$x^2 - 2y^2 = 7 \quad \text{①}$$
$$2x + y = 5 \quad \text{②}$$

SOLUTION

Rearrange equation ② to give y in terms of x	$y = 5 - 2x$
Substitute into equation ①	$x^2 - 2(5 - 2x)^2 = 7$
Multiply out and simplify	$x^2 - 2(25 - 20x + 4x^2) = 7$
	$x^2 - 50 + 40x - 8x^2 = 7$
	$-7x^2 + 40x - 57 = 0$
Multiply through by -1	$7x^2 - 40x + 57 = 0$
Factorise and solve the equation	$(7x - 19)(x - 3) = 0$
	$x = \frac{19}{7}$ or 3
Substitute into equation ②	When $x = \frac{19}{7}, y = 5 - \frac{38}{7} = -\frac{3}{7}$
	When $x = 3, y = 5 - 6 = -1$

The solutions are $x = \frac{19}{7}, y = -\frac{3}{7}$ and $x = 3, y = -1$.

Note that there are two solutions since there are two solutions to a quadratic equation. However, it is also possible that there could be just one repeated solution, or no solutions, since a straight line graph can cross a quadratic graph twice, touch it in one place or not cross it at all.

Two real solutions   One repeated real solution   No real solution

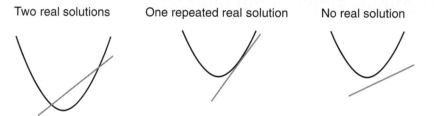

 When you have solved the quadratic equation, always substitute into the linear equation to find the value of the other variable. Substituting into the quadratic equation will give extra solutions which are incorrect.

LINKS

Pure Mathematics	Co-ordinate geometry (C1). May be needed in many other areas of pure mathematics, for example Parametric Equations (C4) and Complex Numbers (FP1).
Mechanics	May be needed in many areas of mechanics, for example Equilibrium Problems (M1 and M2) and Collisions (M2).

Test Yourself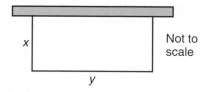

1 Which one of the following is the correct value of x for the linear simultaneous equations
$5x - 3y = 1$ and $3x - 4y = 4$?

A $x = \frac{16}{29}$ **B** $x = \frac{16}{11}$ **C** $x = -\frac{8}{11}$ **D** $x = -\frac{3}{11}$ **E** $x = \frac{5}{29}$

2 Which one of the following is the correct value of y for the linear simultaneous equations
$5x - 2y = 3$ and $y = 1 - 2x$?

A $y = -9$ **B** $y = \frac{5}{9}$ **C** $y = \frac{7}{9}$ **D** $y = -\frac{1}{9}$ **E** $y = -\frac{7}{3}$

3 Look at the simultaneous equations $2x^2 + y^2 = 4$ and $3x + y = 1$.
Which of the following is the quadratic equation which must be solved to find the x values
of the solution?

A $11x^2 - 6x - 3 = 0$ **B** $11x^2 - 3 = 0$ **C** $7x^2 + 6x + 3 = 0$

D $x^2 + 6x + 3 = 0$ **E** $11x^2 + 6x - 3 = 0$

4 Simon is solving the simultaneous equations $y(1 - x) = 1$ and $2x + y = 3$.
Simon's working is shown below.

Rearrange second equation:	$y = 2x - 3$	Line X
Substitute into first equation:	$(2x - 3)(1 - x) = 1$	
	$-2x^2 + 5x - 3 = 1$	Line Y
	$2x^2 - 5x + 4 = 0$	
Discriminant $= -5^2 - 4 \times 2 \times 4 = -25 - 32 = -57$		Line Z
There are no real solutions.		

Simon knows that he must have made at least one mistake, as his teacher has told him
that the equations do have real solutions.
In which line(s) of the working has Simon made a mistake?

A Line X only   **B** Line Y only   **C** Lines Y and Z   **D** Line Z only   **E** Lines X and Z

5 Look at the simultaneous equations $3x^2 + 2y^2 = 5$ and $y - 2x = 1$.
Which one of the following is the correct pair of x values for the solution of these equations?

A $x = \frac{3}{11}$ or $x = -1$ **B** $x = \pm\sqrt{\frac{3}{11}}$ **C** $x = \frac{3}{7}$ or $x = -1$

D $x = -\frac{3}{11}$ or $x = 1$ **E** $x = -\frac{3}{7}$ or $x = 1$

Exam-Style Question

The diagram is a plan view of a rectangular enclosure. A wall forms
one side of the enclosure. The other three sides are formed by fencing
of total length 34 m. The width of the rectangle is x m, the length
is y m, and the area enclosed is 144 m^2.

i) Write down two equations involving x and y and hence show that
$x^2 - 17x + 72 = 0$.
ii) By factorising, solve this equation and find the possible dimensions of the rectangle.

CO-ORDINATE GEOMETRY

2

Two points

A ABOUT THIS TOPIC

Two points define a straight line. This section covers the distance between two points, the gradient of the line joining them and their mid-point. In the next section you will meet the equation of the line.

R REMEMBER

- Co-ordinates from GCSE.
- Pythagoras' theorem from GCSE.

K KEY FACTS

- Gradient of AB $= \dfrac{y_2 - y_1}{x_2 - x_1}$

- Length AB $= \sqrt{(x_2 - x_1)^2 + (y_2 - y_1)^2}$

- Mid-point of AB $= \left(\dfrac{x_1 + x_2}{2}, \dfrac{y_1 + y_2}{2} \right)$

- Parallel lines have the same gradient, $m_1 = m_2$.

- Perpendicular lines have gradients such that $m_1 m_2 = -1$.

  This is sometimes written as: $m_2 = \dfrac{-1}{m_1}$.

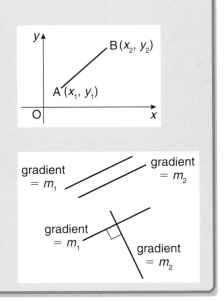

The gradient of a line

The gradient of the line joining A(x_1, y_1) and B(x_2, y_2) is $\dfrac{y_2 - y_1}{x_2 - x_1}$. $\longleftarrow$

This is $\dfrac{\text{difference in } y\text{'s}}{\text{difference in } x\text{'s}}$

EXAMPLE 1

For the points A(5, 2) and B(7, 8) find the gradient of the line AB and the gradient of the line perpendicular to AB.

SOLUTION

Using $m_1 m_2 = -1$ in the form $m_2 = \dfrac{-1}{m_1}$.

Gradient AB $= \dfrac{y_2 - y_1}{x_2 - x_1}$

$= \dfrac{8 - 2}{7 - 5} = \dfrac{6}{2} = 3$

Gradient of perpendicular $= -\dfrac{1}{3}$

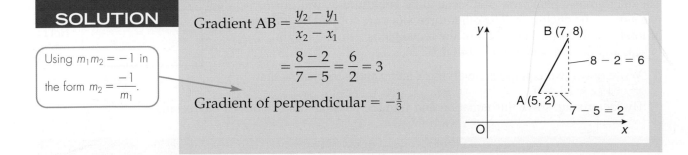

A ADVICE

Always draw a diagram, even if the question does not ask for it.

Mid-point

The mid-point of $A(x_1, y_1)$ and $B(x_2, y_2) = \left(\dfrac{x_1 + x_2}{2}, \dfrac{y_1 + y_2}{2}\right)$.

> The mid-point has x value half-way between the other 2 points' x values (and the same for y).

EXAMPLE 2   Find the mid-point of $A(3, -1)$ and $B(7, 6)$.

SOLUTION

$$\text{Mid-point, M} = \left(\dfrac{x_1 + x_2}{2}, \dfrac{y_1 + y_2}{2}\right)$$

$$= \left(\dfrac{3 + 7}{2}, \dfrac{(-1) + 6}{2}\right)$$

$$= (5, 2.5)$$

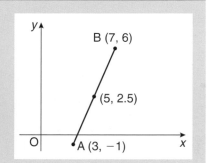

The length of the line joining two points

The length of the line joining $A(x_1, y_1)$ and $B(x_2, y_2)$ is $\sqrt{(x_2 - x_1)^2 + (y_2 - y_1)^2}$.

EXAMPLE 3   What is the length of the line joining $A(-1, 6)$ and $B(6, 2)$?

SOLUTION

Length AB
$$= \sqrt{(x_2 - x_1)^2 + (y_2 - y_1)^2}$$
$$= \sqrt{(6 - (-1))^2 + (2 - 6)^2}$$
$$= \sqrt{(7)^2 + (-4)^2}$$
$$= \sqrt{49 + 16}$$
$$= \sqrt{65}$$

> Length of a line is just Pythagoras' theorem.

A $(-1, 6)$

$2 - 6 = -4$

B $(6, 2)$

$6 - (-1) = 7$

EXAMPLE 4   Three points have co-ordinates $A(-1, 6)$, $B(1, 2)$ and $C(3, y)$.
AB is perpendicular to BC. Find the value of y.

SOLUTION

$$\text{Gradient AB} = \frac{2 - 6}{1 - (-1)} = \frac{-4}{2} = -2$$

$$\therefore \text{Gradient BC} = \frac{-1}{-2} = \frac{1}{2}$$

> Find the gradient of BC using:
> $$\frac{-1}{\text{gradient of AB}}.$$

$$\frac{y - 2}{3 - 1} = \frac{1}{2}$$

$$\text{so } \frac{y - 2}{2} = \frac{1}{2}$$

> Write out the formula for the gradient of the line joining B and C (with y in it).

$$y - 2 = 1$$

$$y = 3$$

EXAMPLE 5

A quadrilateral has vertices A(1, −2), B(4, 0), C(2, 3) and D(−1, 1).
i) Draw the quadrilateral ABCD.
ii) Find the gradients of lines AB, BC, CD and DA.
iii) Find the lengths of AB, BC, CD and DA.
iv) What do ii) and iii) tell you about ABCD?
v) What is the area of ABCD?

SOLUTION

i)

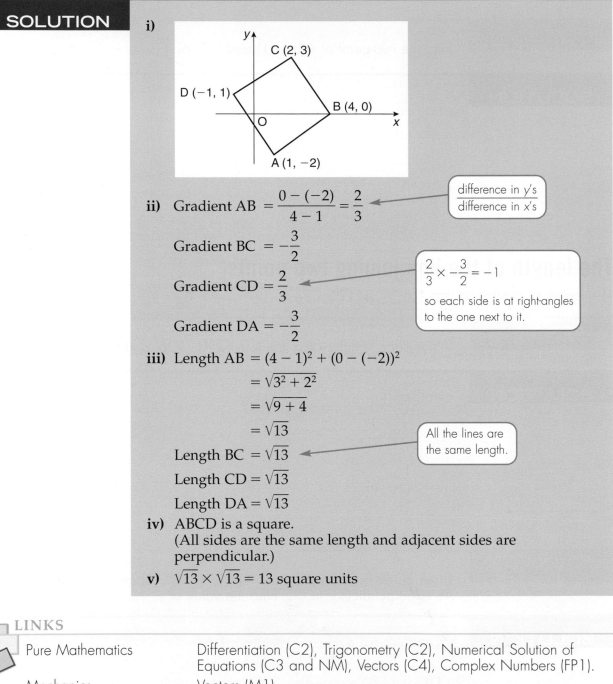

ii) Gradient AB $= \dfrac{0-(-2)}{4-1} = \dfrac{2}{3}$

difference in y's / difference in x's

Gradient BC $= -\dfrac{3}{2}$

Gradient CD $= \dfrac{2}{3}$

$\dfrac{2}{3} \times -\dfrac{3}{2} = -1$

so each side is at right-angles to the one next to it.

Gradient DA $= -\dfrac{3}{2}$

iii) Length AB $= (4-1)^2 + (0-(-2))^2$

$\qquad = \sqrt{3^2 + 2^2}$

$\qquad = \sqrt{9+4}$

$\qquad = \sqrt{13}$

Length BC $= \sqrt{13}$

All the lines are the same length.

Length CD $= \sqrt{13}$

Length DA $= \sqrt{13}$

iv) ABCD is a square.
(All sides are the same length and adjacent sides are perpendicular.)

v) $\sqrt{13} \times \sqrt{13} = 13$ square units

LINKS

Pure Mathematics	Differentiation (C2), Trigonometry (C2), Numerical Solution of Equations (C3 and NM), Vectors (C4), Complex Numbers (FP1).
Mechanics	Vectors (M1).
Decision Mathematics	Linear Programming (D1).

Test Yourself ▶L

1 The points A and B have co-ordinates $(-1, 4)$ and $(3, -2)$. What is the gradient of the line joining A to B?

A -3 **B** $-\frac{2}{3}$ **C** -1 **D** -1.5 **E** 1.5

2 The mid-point of the line AB is $(-2, 1)$. The co-ordinates of point B are $(1, -1)$. What are the co-ordinates of A?

A $(-5, 3)$ **B** $(-3, 3)$ **C** $(-0.5, 0)$ **D** $(4, -3)$ **E** $(-5, 1)$

3 The points A and B have co-ordinates $(-3, 1)$ and $(2, 5)$. Find the length of the line AB.

A 3 **B** $\sqrt{41}$ **C** $\sqrt{17}$ **D** 41 **E** 5

4 The trapezium PQRS has vertices $P(0, 1)$, $Q(6, 4)$, $R(4, z)$ and $S(0, 5)$. What is the value of z?

A 13 **B** 7 **C** 8
D $4\frac{1}{3}$ **E** 5

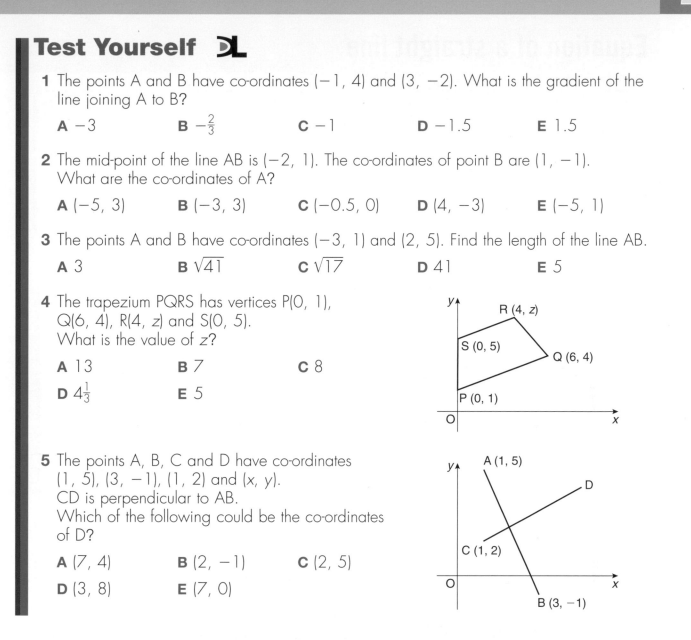

5 The points A, B, C and D have co-ordinates $(1, 5)$, $(3, -1)$, $(1, 2)$ and (x, y). CD is perpendicular to AB. Which of the following could be the co-ordinates of D?

A $(7, 4)$ **B** $(2, -1)$ **C** $(2, 5)$
D $(3, 8)$ **E** $(7, 0)$

Exam-Style Question ▶L

$A(2, 7)$, $B(6, -1)$ and $C(0, 1)$ are three points.

i) M is the mid-point of AB. Find the co-ordinates of M.

ii) Find the exact values of the lengths of the lines AB and CM.

iii) Show that AB and CM are perpendicular and hence find the area of the triangle ABC.

Equation of a straight line

The equation of a straight line, often just referred to as the equation of a line, is useful in many areas of mathematics. The most common form is $y = mx + c$; however, there are other forms of the equation of a line that you need to know.

- Co-ordinates from GCSE.
- The gradient of a line joining two points from C1.
- The gradient of parallel and perpendicular lines from C1.

- In the equation of the line $y = mx + c$,
  m is the gradient and
  c is the intercept with the y axis.

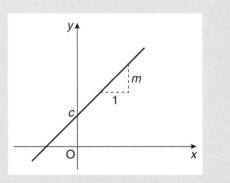

- The equation of the line with gradient m passing through the point (x_1, y_1) is
  $y - y_1 = m(x - x_1)$.

- The equation of the line passing through the points (x_1, y_1) and (x_2, y_2) is
  $$\frac{y - y_1}{y_2 - y_1} = \frac{x - x_1}{x_2 - x_1}.$$

- The equation of a line can also be written as $ax + by + c = 0$, which is commonly written so a, b and c are integers.

- Vertical lines have equation $x = a$.
  These lines are parallel to the y axis.

- Horizontal lines have equation $y = b$.
  These lines are parallel to the x axis.

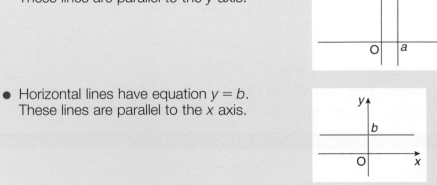

EXAMPLE 1

Sketch the following lines.
i) $y = 3x + 1$
ii) $x = 1$
iii) $3x + 2y = 12$
iv) $y = -3$

Note that *sketching* is different from *plotting*. A sketch should just show the general shape of the graph and any important points.

SOLUTION

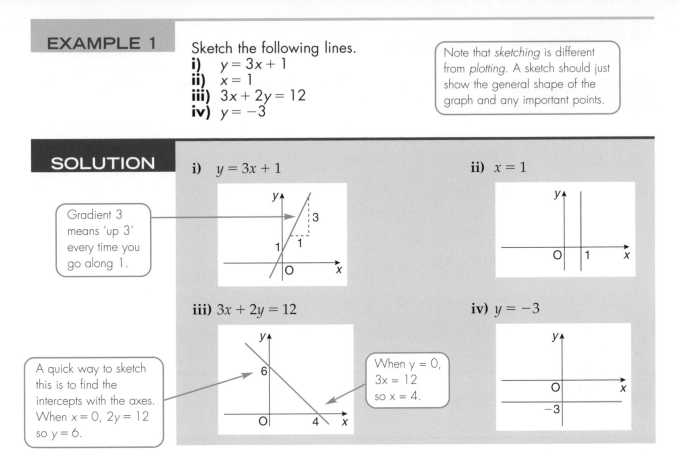

i) $y = 3x + 1$

Gradient 3 means 'up 3' every time you go along 1.

ii) $x = 1$

iii) $3x + 2y = 12$

A quick way to sketch this is to find the intercepts with the axes. When $x = 0$, $2y = 12$ so $y = 6$.

When $y = 0$, $3x = 12$ so $x = 4$.

iv) $y = -3$

Finding the equation of a line

The equation of a line can be found by obtaining its gradient, substituting this value in for m in $y = mx + c$ and then finding c by substituting a point into the resulting equation.

Alternatively, if the gradient of the line m and a point (x_1, y_1) are known, the equation of the line can be found with $y - y_1 = m(x - x_1)$.

If two points on the line are known the equation can be found with
$$\frac{y - y_1}{y_2 - y_1} = \frac{x - x_1}{x_2 - x_1}.$$

EXAMPLE 2

Find the equation of the line parallel to $y = 3x + 2$ through $(1, -5)$.

SOLUTION

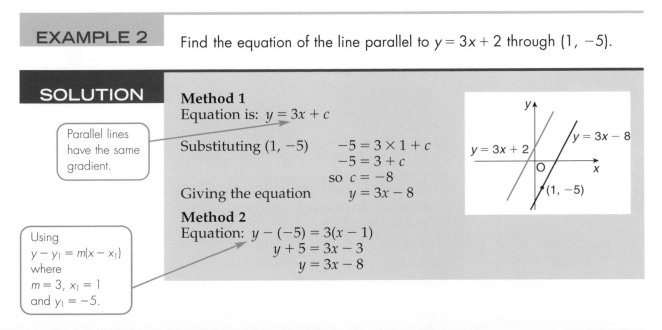

Method 1
Equation is: $y = 3x + c$

Parallel lines have the same gradient.

Substituting $(1, -5)$ $-5 = 3 \times 1 + c$
                           $-5 = 3 + c$
                    so $c = -8$
Giving the equation $y = 3x - 8$

Method 2
Equation: $y - (-5) = 3(x - 1)$
          $y + 5 = 3x - 3$
          $y = 3x - 8$

Using
$y - y_1 = m(x - x_1)$
where
$m = 3$, $x_1 = 1$
and $y_1 = -5$.

EXAMPLE 3

Find the equation of the line perpendicular to $y = -2x + 1$ through $(4, 0)$.

SOLUTION

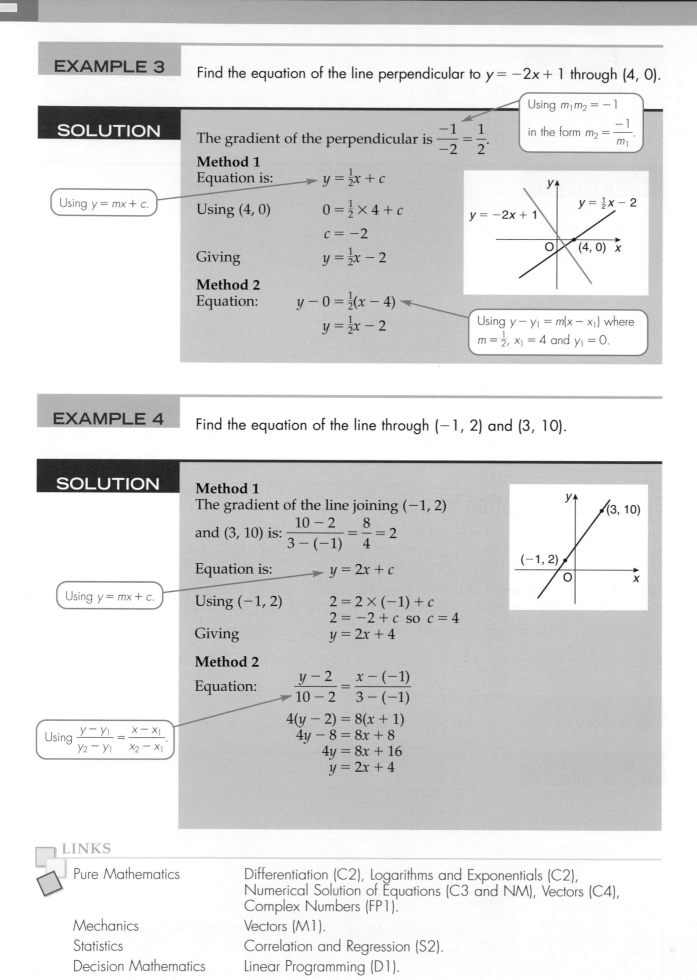

The gradient of the perpendicular is $\dfrac{-1}{-2} = \dfrac{1}{2}$.

> Using $m_1 m_2 = -1$ in the form $m_2 = \dfrac{-1}{m_1}$.

Method 1

Equation is: $y = \frac{1}{2}x + c$

> Using $y = mx + c$.

Using $(4, 0)$ $0 = \frac{1}{2} \times 4 + c$

$c = -2$

Giving $y = \frac{1}{2}x - 2$

Method 2

Equation: $y - 0 = \frac{1}{2}(x - 4)$

$y = \frac{1}{2}x - 2$

> Using $y - y_1 = m(x - x_1)$ where $m = \frac{1}{2}$, $x_1 = 4$ and $y_1 = 0$.

EXAMPLE 4

Find the equation of the line through $(-1, 2)$ and $(3, 10)$.

SOLUTION

Method 1

The gradient of the line joining $(-1, 2)$ and $(3, 10)$ is: $\dfrac{10 - 2}{3 - (-1)} = \dfrac{8}{4} = 2$

Equation is: $y = 2x + c$

> Using $y = mx + c$.

Using $(-1, 2)$ $2 = 2 \times (-1) + c$

$2 = -2 + c$ so $c = 4$

Giving $y = 2x + 4$

Method 2

Equation: $\dfrac{y - 2}{10 - 2} = \dfrac{x - (-1)}{3 - (-1)}$

$4(y - 2) = 8(x + 1)$

$4y - 8 = 8x + 8$

$4y = 8x + 16$

$y = 2x + 4$

> Using $\dfrac{y - y_1}{y_2 - y_1} = \dfrac{x - x_1}{x_2 - x_1}$.

LINKS

Pure Mathematics	Differentiation (C2), Logarithms and Exponentials (C2), Numerical Solution of Equations (C3 and NM), Vectors (C4), Complex Numbers (FP1).
Mechanics	Vectors (M1).
Statistics	Correlation and Regression (S2).
Decision Mathematics	Linear Programming (D1).

Test Yourself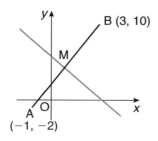

1 Find the equation of the line through $(-1, 3)$ and $(2, -3)$.

A $y = -6x - 3$ **B** $y = -2x + 5$ **C** $y = -2x + 1$

D $y = 2x + 5$ **E** $y = -6x + 17$

2 A line has equation $5x - 7y + 2 = 0$. Find its gradient.

A $-\frac{5}{7}$ **B** 5 **C** $\frac{5}{7}$ **D** $-\frac{7}{5}$ **E** $\frac{7}{5}$

3 Which of these is the equation of the line in the diagram?

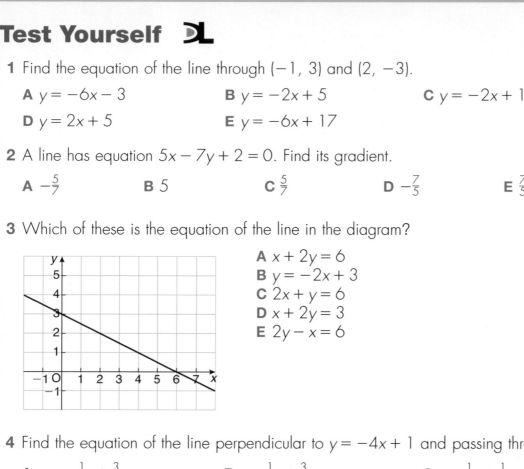

A $x + 2y = 6$
B $y = -2x + 3$
C $2x + y = 6$
D $x + 2y = 3$
E $2y - x = 6$

4 Find the equation of the line perpendicular to $y = -4x + 1$ and passing through $(2, 1)$.

A $y = -\frac{1}{4}x + \frac{3}{2}$ **B** $y = \frac{1}{4}x + \frac{3}{2}$ **C** $y = \frac{1}{4}x + \frac{1}{2}$

D $y = 4x - 7$ **E** $y = \frac{1}{4}x + \frac{7}{4}$

5 The line L is parallel to $y = 3x - 2$ and passes through the point $(-2, -1)$. Find the co-ordinates of the point of intersection with the x axis.

A $(-\frac{1}{3}, 0)$ **B** $(-\frac{5}{3}, 0)$ **C** $(0, 5)$ **D** $(\frac{7}{3}, 0)$ **E** $(\frac{2}{3}, 0)$

Exam-Style Question

A and B are points with co-ordinates $(-1, -2)$ and $(3, 10)$ respectively.

i) Find the co-ordinates of the mid-point, M, of AB.
Show also that the equation of the perpendicular bisector of AB is $x + 3y = 13$.

ii) Find the area of the triangle bounded by the perpendicular bisector, the y axis and the line AM.

Circles

The equation of a circle is based on Pythagoras' theorem. The equation is formed by using the fact that any point on the circle (x, y) will be a fixed distance (the radius) from the centre of the circle. This might be the first time you have met a graph whose equation has x and y on the same side. It is a very common topic for examination questions.

- Pythagoras' theorem from GCSE.
- Co-ordinates from GCSE.
- Length, gradient and mid-point of a line joining two points from C1.

- The equation of a circle with radius r and centre at the origin is
  $x^2 + y^2 = r^2$.

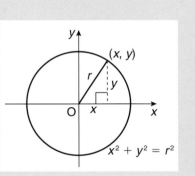

- The equation of a circle with radius r and centre at (a, b) is
  $(x - a)^2 + (y - b)^2 = r^2$.

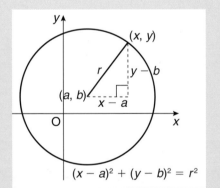

- The angle in a semi-circle is a right angle.
- The perpendicular from the centre of a circle to a chord bisects the chord.
- The tangent to a circle at a point is perpendicular to the radius through that point.

EXAMPLE 1

Give the centre and radius of the circle with equation $(x + 2)^2 + (y - 4)^2 = 16$.

> Use the formula $(x - a)^2 + (y - b)^2 = r^2$.
> $(x + 2)^2$ is the same as $(x - (-2))^2$ so the x co-ordinate of the centre is -2.

SOLUTION

The centre is at $(-2, 4)$.
$r^2 = 16 \Rightarrow r = 4$ so the radius is 4.

EXAMPLE 2

Show that the circle with equation $x^2 + y^2 - 8x + 2y - 8 = 0$ has centre $(4, -1)$ and radius 5.

SOLUTION

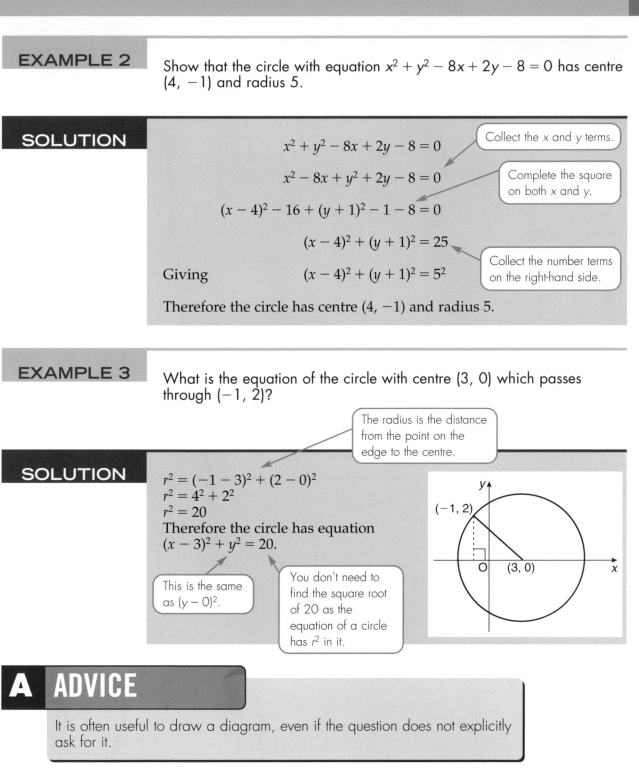

$$x^2 + y^2 - 8x + 2y - 8 = 0$$

Collect the x and y terms.

$$x^2 - 8x + y^2 + 2y - 8 = 0$$

Complete the square on both x and y.

$$(x - 4)^2 - 16 + (y + 1)^2 - 1 - 8 = 0$$

$$(x - 4)^2 + (y + 1)^2 = 25$$

Collect the number terms on the right-hand side.

Giving

$$(x - 4)^2 + (y + 1)^2 = 5^2$$

Therefore the circle has centre $(4, -1)$ and radius 5.

EXAMPLE 3

What is the equation of the circle with centre $(3, 0)$ which passes through $(-1, 2)$?

The radius is the distance from the point on the edge to the centre.

SOLUTION

$r^2 = (-1 - 3)^2 + (2 - 0)^2$
$r^2 = 4^2 + 2^2$
$r^2 = 20$
Therefore the circle has equation
$(x - 3)^2 + y^2 = 20$.

This is the same as $(y - 0)^2$.

You don't need to find the square root of 20 as the equation of a circle has r^2 in it.

A ADVICE

It is often useful to draw a diagram, even if the question does not explicitly ask for it.

In the next example you find the equation of the tangent to the circle. The method depends on the fact that the tangent at the point of contact is at right angles to the radius.

EXAMPLE 4

Find the equation of the tangent to the circle $(x - 1)^2 + (y + 3)^2 = 10$ at the point $(4, -2)$.

SOLUTION

The gradient of the radius joining the centre $(1, -3)$ to $(4, -2)$ is:

$$\frac{y_2 - y_1}{x_2 - x_1} = \frac{(-2) - (-3)}{4 - 1} = \frac{1}{3}$$

So the gradient of the tangent is m_2 where

> Using $m_1 m_2 = -1$ for lines at right angles.

$$\frac{1}{3} \times m_2 = -1$$

so $m_2 = -3$

Therefore the line has equation $y = -3x + c$.

$(4, -2)$ is on the line
so $-2 = -3 \times 4 + c$
giving $c = 10$.

The tangent has equation $y = -3x + 10$.

> The tangent is at right angles to the radius. Start by finding the gradient of the radius.

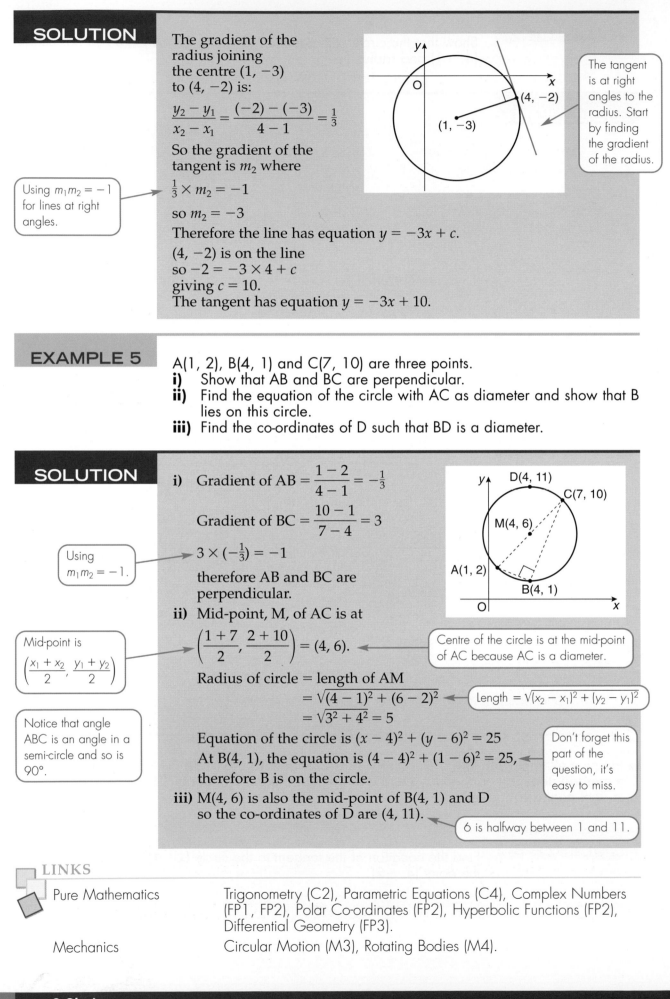

EXAMPLE 5

$A(1, 2)$, $B(4, 1)$ and $C(7, 10)$ are three points.
i) Show that AB and BC are perpendicular.
ii) Find the equation of the circle with AC as diameter and show that B lies on this circle.
iii) Find the co-ordinates of D such that BD is a diameter.

SOLUTION

i) Gradient of $AB = \dfrac{1 - 2}{4 - 1} = -\dfrac{1}{3}$

Gradient of $BC = \dfrac{10 - 1}{7 - 4} = 3$

> Using $m_1 m_2 = -1$.

$$3 \times \left(-\frac{1}{3}\right) = -1$$

therefore AB and BC are perpendicular.

ii) Mid-point, M, of AC is at

> Mid-point is
> $\left(\dfrac{x_1 + x_2}{2}, \dfrac{y_1 + y_2}{2}\right)$

$$\left(\frac{1 + 7}{2}, \frac{2 + 10}{2}\right) = (4, 6).$$

> Centre of the circle is at the mid-point of AC because AC is a diameter.

Radius of circle $=$ length of AM

$$= \sqrt{(4 - 1)^2 + (6 - 2)^2}$$

> Length $= \sqrt{(x_2 - x_1)^2 + (y_2 - y_1)^2}$

$$= \sqrt{3^2 + 4^2} = 5$$

> Notice that angle ABC is an angle in a semi-circle and so is $90°$.

Equation of the circle is $(x - 4)^2 + (y - 6)^2 = 25$

At $B(4, 1)$, the equation is $(4 - 4)^2 + (1 - 6)^2 = 25$,

therefore B is on the circle.

> Don't forget this part of the question, it's easy to miss.

iii) $M(4, 6)$ is also the mid-point of $B(4, 1)$ and D so the co-ordinates of D are $(4, 11)$.

> 6 is halfway between 1 and 11.

☐ LINKS

Pure Mathematics	Trigonometry (C2), Parametric Equations (C4), Complex Numbers (FP1, FP2), Polar Co-ordinates (FP2), Hyperbolic Functions (FP2), Differential Geometry (FP3).
Mechanics	Circular Motion (M3), Rotating Bodies (M4).

Test Yourself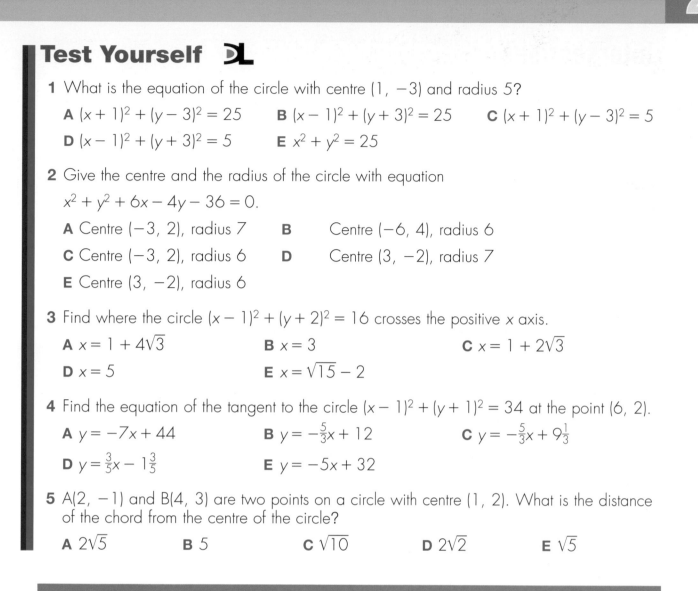

1 What is the equation of the circle with centre $(1, -3)$ and radius 5?

A $(x + 1)^2 + (y - 3)^2 = 25$ **B** $(x - 1)^2 + (y + 3)^2 = 25$ **C** $(x + 1)^2 + (y - 3)^2 = 5$

D $(x - 1)^2 + (y + 3)^2 = 5$ **E** $x^2 + y^2 = 25$

2 Give the centre and the radius of the circle with equation

$x^2 + y^2 + 6x - 4y - 36 = 0$.

A Centre $(-3, 2)$, radius 7   **B**   Centre $(-6, 4)$, radius 6

C Centre $(-3, 2)$, radius 6   **D**   Centre $(3, -2)$, radius 7

E Centre $(3, -2)$, radius 6

3 Find where the circle $(x - 1)^2 + (y + 2)^2 = 16$ crosses the positive x axis.

A $x = 1 + 4\sqrt{3}$ **B** $x = 3$ **C** $x = 1 + 2\sqrt{3}$

D $x = 5$ **E** $x = \sqrt{15} - 2$

4 Find the equation of the tangent to the circle $(x - 1)^2 + (y + 1)^2 = 34$ at the point $(6, 2)$.

A $y = -7x + 44$ **B** $y = -\frac{5}{3}x + 12$ **C** $y = -\frac{5}{3}x + 9\frac{1}{3}$

D $y = \frac{3}{5}x - 1\frac{3}{5}$ **E** $y = -5x + 32$

5 $A(2, -1)$ and $B(4, 3)$ are two points on a circle with centre $(1, 2)$. What is the distance of the chord from the centre of the circle?

A $2\sqrt{5}$ **B** 5 **C** $\sqrt{10}$ **D** $2\sqrt{2}$ **E** $\sqrt{5}$

Exam-Style Question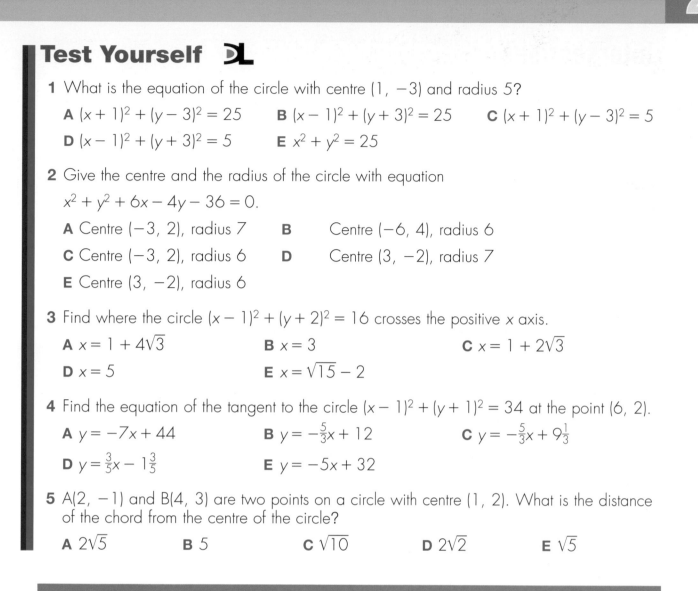

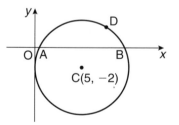

The figure shows a circle with centre $C(5, -2)$ and radius 5.

i)   Show that the equation of the circle may be written as
$x^2 + y^2 - 10x + 4y + 4 = 0$.

ii) Find the co-ordinates of the points A and B where the circle cuts the x axis.
Leave your answers in surd form.

iii) Verify that the point $D(8, 2)$ lies on the circle.
Find the equation of the tangent to the circle at D in the form $y = mx + c$.

Intersections

It is often important to be able to find where two graphs cross. The graphs could be two straight lines, a line and a curve or two curves. You should already know how to solve simultaneous equations; finding the points of intersection of two graphs is simply an application of this.

- Equation of a line from GCSE and C1.
- Quadratic equations from GCSE and C1.
- Equation of a circle from C1.
- Simultaneous equations: linear and quadratic from C1.

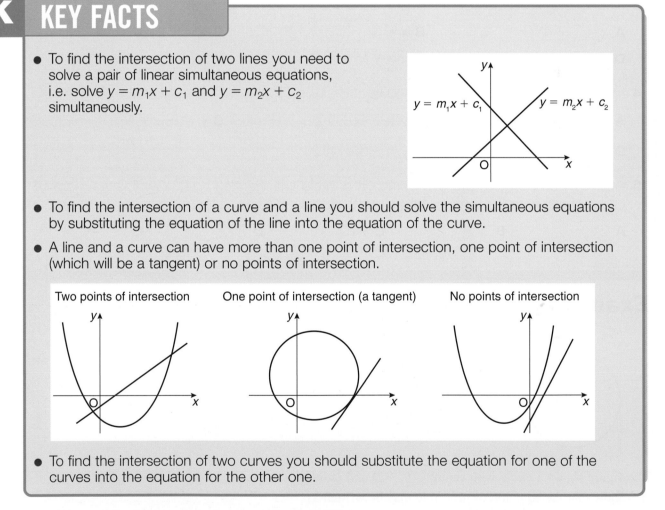

- To find the intersection of two lines you need to solve a pair of linear simultaneous equations, i.e. solve $y = m_1x + c_1$ and $y = m_2x + c_2$ simultaneously.

- To find the intersection of a curve and a line you should solve the simultaneous equations by substituting the equation of the line into the equation of the curve.

- A line and a curve can have more than one point of intersection, one point of intersection (which will be a tangent) or no points of intersection.

Two points of intersection   One point of intersection (a tangent)   No points of intersection

- To find the intersection of two curves you should substitute the equation for one of the curves into the equation for the other one.

Finding the intersection of two lines

EXAMPLE 1

Sketch the lines $x + 3y = 11$ and $3x + 2y = 12$ on the same axes, and find the co-ordinates of the point where they intersect.

SOLUTION

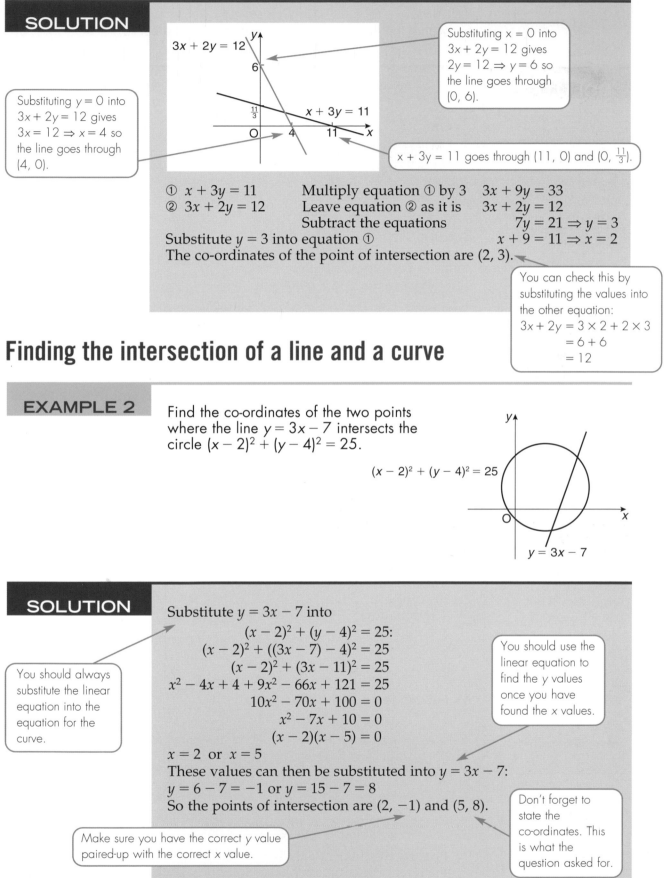

Substituting $y = 0$ into $3x + 2y = 12$ gives $3x = 12 \Rightarrow x = 4$ so the line goes through $(4, 0)$.

Substituting $x = 0$ into $3x + 2y = 12$ gives $2y = 12 \Rightarrow y = 6$ so the line goes through $(0, 6)$.

$x + 3y = 11$ goes through $(11, 0)$ and $(0, \frac{11}{3})$.

① $x + 3y = 11$ Multiply equation ① by 3 $3x + 9y = 33$
② $3x + 2y = 12$ Leave equation ② as it is $3x + 2y = 12$
                      Subtract the equations $7y = 21 \Rightarrow y = 3$
Substitute $y = 3$ into equation ① $x + 9 = 11 \Rightarrow x = 2$
The co-ordinates of the point of intersection are $(2, 3)$.

You can check this by substituting the values into the other equation:
$3x + 2y = 3 \times 2 + 2 \times 3$
$\qquad\qquad = 6 + 6$
$\qquad\qquad = 12$

Finding the intersection of a line and a curve

EXAMPLE 2

Find the co-ordinates of the two points where the line $y = 3x - 7$ intersects the circle $(x - 2)^2 + (y - 4)^2 = 25$.

$(x - 2)^2 + (y - 4)^2 = 25$

$y = 3x - 7$

SOLUTION

Substitute $y = 3x - 7$ into
$$(x - 2)^2 + (y - 4)^2 = 25:$$
$$(x - 2)^2 + ((3x - 7) - 4)^2 = 25$$
$$(x - 2)^2 + (3x - 11)^2 = 25$$
$$x^2 - 4x + 4 + 9x^2 - 66x + 121 = 25$$
$$10x^2 - 70x + 100 = 0$$
$$x^2 - 7x + 10 = 0$$
$$(x - 2)(x - 5) = 0$$
$x = 2$ or $x = 5$
These values can then be substituted into $y = 3x - 7$:
$y = 6 - 7 = -1$ or $y = 15 - 7 = 8$
So the points of intersection are $(2, -1)$ and $(5, 8)$.

You should always substitute the linear equation into the equation for the curve.

You should use the linear equation to find the y values once you have found the x values.

Make sure you have the correct y value paired-up with the correct x value.

Don't forget to state the co-ordinates. This is what the question asked for.

EXAMPLE 3

Show that the line $y = 2x - 7$ is a tangent to the curve $y = x^2 - 2x - 3$.

SOLUTION

> You should always substitute the linear equation into the equation for the curve.

Substituting $y = 2x - 7$ into $y = x^2 - 2x - 3$

$$2x - 7 = x^2 - 2x - 3$$
$$0 = x^2 - 4x + 4$$
$$0 = (x - 2)(x - 2)$$
$$x = 2 \text{ (repeated root)}$$

Substituting $x = 2$ into $y = 2x - 7$ gives:

$$y = 4 - 7$$
$$y = -3$$

The co-ordinates of the point of intersection are $(2, -3)$. There is a single (repeated) point of intersection and therefore the line is a tangent.

> If you have studied differentiation in C2 you should know a different way to tackle this question.

EXAMPLE 4

The circle $(x + 1)^2 + (y - 2)^2 = 16$ is shown.

i) Find the equations of the two tangents to the circle which are parallel to the y axis.

ii) Show that the line $y = x - 4$ does not intersect the circle.

$(x + 1)^2 + (y - 2)^2 = 16$

SOLUTION

> The tangents parallel to the y axis are vertical lines of the form $x = $ constant.

i) The centre of the circle is at $(-1, 2)$.
The radius of the circle is $\sqrt{16} = 4$.
The lines are both distance 4 from the centre.
The equations of the tangents are:
$x = -5$ and $x = 3$.

> This is a quadratic equation, so expand it and set it equal to 0.

ii) Substitute $y = x - 4$ into

$$(x + 1)^2 + (y - 2)^2 = 16$$
$$(x + 1)^2 + (x - 4 - 2)^2 = 16$$
$$(x + 1)^2 + (x - 6)^2 = 16$$
$$x^2 + 2x + 1 + x^2 - 12x + 36 - 16 = 0$$
$$2x^2 - 10x + 21 = 0$$

This has discriminant

> The discriminant is the bit under the square root in the quadratic equation formula:
> $$x = \frac{-b \pm \sqrt{b^2 - 4ac}}{2a}$$

$$(-10)^2 - 4 \times 2 \times 21 = 100 - 168$$
$$= -68$$

Because the discriminant is negative the quadratic equation has no solutions, so the line and circle do not intersect.

Finding the intersection of two curves

EXAMPLE 5   Show that the graphs of $y = 2x^2 - 8x + 5$ and $y = x^2 - 4x + 2$ intersect twice and find the co-ordinates of the two points of intersection.

SOLUTION

This just means that you set the two expressions for y equal to each other, to find the points where the two curves intersect.

Equating the two expressions for y
$$2x^2 - 8x + 5 = x^2 - 4x + 2$$
$$x^2 - 4x + 3 = 0$$
$$(x - 1)(x - 3) = 0$$
This gives $x = 1$ or $x = 3$
Substituting into $y = x^2 - 4x + 2$
$$x = 1 \Rightarrow y = 1 - 4 + 2 = -1$$
$$x = 3 \Rightarrow y = 9 - 12 + 2 = -1$$
So there are two points of intersection, at $(1, -1)$ and $(3, -1)$.

LINKS

Pure Mathematics   Differentiation (C2), Integration (C2), Numerical Solution of Equations (C3 and NM), Complex Numbers (FP1).

Statistics   Correlation and Regression (S2).

Decision Mathematics   Linear Programming (D1).

Test Yourself ◗L

1 Find the co-ordinates of the point where the lines $2x + 3y = 12$ and $3x - y = 7$ intersect.

   A $\left(\frac{9}{7}, \frac{22}{7}\right)$ **B** $(3, 2)$ **C** $(9, 2)$ **D** $(3, 6)$ **E** $\left(\frac{33}{8}, \frac{5}{4}\right)$

2 Find the co-ordinates of the points where the line $y = 2x + 3$ intersects the curve $y = x^2 + 3x + 1$.

   A $(-2, 5)$ and $(1, -1)$ **B** $(-4, -5)$ and $(-1, 1)$ **C** $(-2, -9)$ and $(1, 5)$

   D $(-1, 1)$ and $(2, 7)$ **E** $(-2, -1)$ and $(1, 5)$

3 Find the equations of the two tangents to the circle $(x - 2)^2 + (y + 1)^2 = 9$ which are parallel to the x axis.

   A $x = -5$ and $x = 1$ **B** $x = 5$ and $x = -1$ **C** $y = 8$ and $y = -10$

   D $y = 4$ and $y = -2$ **E** $y = 2$ and $y = -4$

4 Which of the following lines does **not** intersect the circle $x^2 - 8x + y^2 - 9 = 0$ shown in the diagram?

   A $y = 2x + 2$ **B** $y = -5$

   C $y = 2x + 4$ **D** $y = x - 1$

   E $x = 7$

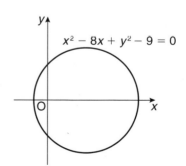

5 How many points of intersection are there between the curve $y = x^2 - 3$ and the circle $x^2 + y^2 = 9$?

    A 0   **B** 1   **C** 2   **D** 3   **E** 4

Exam-Style Question ⊃L

i)   Find the co-ordinates of the points where the graph of $y = x^2 + 2x - 3$ crosses the axes and sketch the graph.

ii)   Show that the graphs of $y = x^2 + 2x - 3$ and $y = x^2 - 10x + 21$ intersect only once and find the co-ordinates of the point of intersection.

iii)   Show that the line $y = -2x - 8$ does not intersect either curve.

POLYNOMIALS

3

Polynomial addition, subtraction and multiplication

'Poly' comes from a Greek word meaning 'many'. Polynomials are expressions involving many terms and you will use them everywhere in pure mathematics.

You have to be able to add, subtract and multiply polynomials confidently.

- Quadratic functions from GCSE and C1.
- Simplifying expressions and collecting like terms from GCSE.
- Opening (removing) brackets from GCSE.
- Factorising expressions from GCSE and C1.

K KEY FACTS

- Examples of polynomials in terms of x, up to order 5:

Order 1	$2x - 5$	linear
Order 2	$3x^2 - 11x + 7$	quadratic
Order 3	$x^3 + 6x^2 + 11x + 6$	cubic
Order 4	$2x^4 - 3x^3 + 6x^2 - 7x + 8$	quartic
Order 5	$x^5 + 3x^4 - 5x^3 + x^2 - 3x + 6$	quintic

- The order of the polynomial is the highest power of the variable it contains.
  So $4 - 7x^5 + 3x^{12}$ has order 12.

- The polynomial $2x^4 - 3x^2 + x - 1$ can also be written as $f(x) = 2x^4 - 3x^2 + x - 1$ and $f(0)$ means $f(0) = 2 \times (0)^4 - 3 \times (0)^2 + 0 - 1 = -1$.

- There are two common ways of setting out work with polynomials, either in columns where like terms go in the same column, or in a line where you collect like terms together.

Adding polynomials

Adding polynomials is the same as collecting like terms – add and subtract those with identical powers and letters.

EXAMPLE 1

Add $2x^3 - 7x^2 + 4x - 5$ and $x^3 + 9x - 7$.

SOLUTION

Method 1: Using columns: set up the polynomials in columns and line up the terms.

x^3 means $1x^3$ or the coefficient of x^3 is 1.

$$
\begin{array}{rrrr}
2x^3 & -7x^2 & +4x & -5 \\
+ \ (x^3 & & +9x & -7) \\
\hline
3x^3 & -7x^2 & +13x & -12
\end{array}
$$

⚠ There is no term of x^2 in the second polynomial.

Method 2: Collecting like terms:

$$(2x^3 - 7x^2 + 4x - 5) + (x^3 + 9x - 7)$$
$$= (2x^3 + x^3) + (-7x^2) + (4x + 9x) + (-5 - 7)$$
$$= 3x^3 - 7x^2 + 13x - 12$$

⚠ Look at the term $+ (-7x^2)$. Notice how the '$-$' sign goes with $7x^2$ inside the brackets.

Subtracting polynomials

EXAMPLE 2

Subtract $(x^3 + 5x - 3)$ from $(3x^3 + 3x^2 + 4x + 5)$.

SOLUTION

Method 1: Using columns:

$$
\begin{array}{rrrr}
3x^3 & +3x^2 & +4x & +5 \\
- \ (x^3 & & +5x & -3) \\
\hline
2x^3 & +3x^2 & -x & +8
\end{array}
$$

⚠ A '$-$' sign in front of the brackets means that you have to multiply each term in the brackets by -1 or change the sign in front of each term in the brackets.
Remember $- -3 = +3$.

Method 2: Collecting like terms:

$$(3x^3 + 3x^2 + 4x + 5) - (x^3 + 5x - 3)$$
$$= 3x^3 + 3x^2 + 4x + 5 - x^3 - 5x + 3$$
$$= (3x^3 - x^3) + (+3x^2) + (4x - 5x) + (5 + 3)$$
$$= 2x^3 + 3x^2 - x + 8$$

Change the signs first

Multiplying polynomials

 Remember that x means x^1.
Remember that when you multiply powers of x you add the indices: $x^3 \times x^5 = x^{3+5} = x^8$.
Remember the rules for multiplying positive and negative numbers are:
$+ \times + = +; \quad - \times - = +; \quad + \times - = -; \quad - \times + = -;$

EXAMPLE 3 Multiply $x - 2$ by $4x^2 - 3x + 2$.

SOLUTION

Method 1: Using columns:

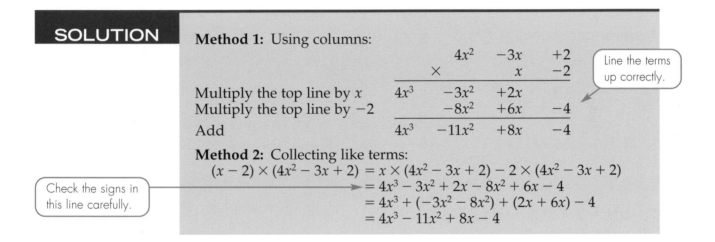

Line the terms up correctly.

	$4x^2$	$-3x$	$+2$
$\times$		x	-2

Multiply the top line by x $4x^3 \quad -3x^2 \quad +2x$
Multiply the top line by -2 $-8x^2 \quad +6x \quad -4$

Add $4x^3 \quad -11x^2 \quad +8x \quad -4$

Method 2: Collecting like terms:

Check the signs in this line carefully.

$$(x - 2) \times (4x^2 - 3x + 2) = x \times (4x^2 - 3x + 2) - 2 \times (4x^2 - 3x + 2)$$
$$= 4x^3 - 3x^2 + 2x - 8x^2 + 6x - 4$$
$$= 4x^3 + (-3x^2 - 8x^2) + (2x + 6x) - 4$$
$$= 4x^3 - 11x^2 + 8x - 4$$

□ LINKS

Pure Mathematics	Solving Equations.
	Sketching Curves.
	Binomial Expansions (C1 and C4).
Differential Equations	Solving Equations.
Numerical Methods	Solving Equations.
Statistics	Binomial distribution (S1).

Test Yourself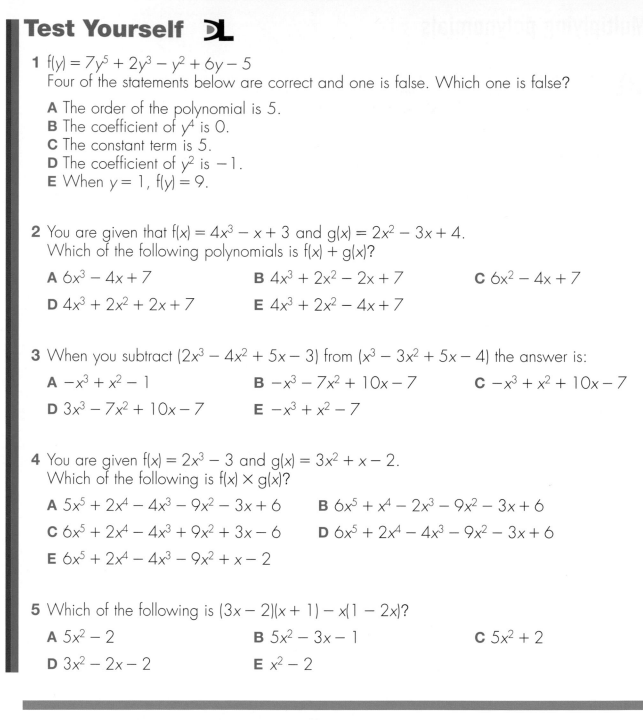

1 $f(y) = 7y^5 + 2y^3 - y^2 + 6y - 5$
  Four of the statements below are correct and one is false. Which one is false?

  A The order of the polynomial is 5.
  B The coefficient of y^4 is 0.
  C The constant term is 5.
  D The coefficient of y^2 is -1.
  E When $y = 1$, $f(y) = 9$.

2 You are given that $f(x) = 4x^3 - x + 3$ and $g(x) = 2x^2 - 3x + 4$.
  Which of the following polynomials is $f(x) + g(x)$?

  A $6x^3 - 4x + 7$ B $4x^3 + 2x^2 - 2x + 7$ C $6x^2 - 4x + 7$

  D $4x^3 + 2x^2 + 2x + 7$ E $4x^3 + 2x^2 - 4x + 7$

3 When you subtract $(2x^3 - 4x^2 + 5x - 3)$ from $(x^3 - 3x^2 + 5x - 4)$ the answer is:

  A $-x^3 + x^2 - 1$ B $-x^3 - 7x^2 + 10x - 7$ C $-x^3 + x^2 + 10x - 7$

  D $3x^3 - 7x^2 + 10x - 7$ E $-x^3 + x^2 - 7$

4 You are given $f(x) = 2x^3 - 3$ and $g(x) = 3x^2 + x - 2$.
  Which of the following is $f(x) \times g(x)$?

  A $5x^5 + 2x^4 - 4x^3 - 9x^2 - 3x + 6$ B $6x^5 + x^4 - 2x^3 - 9x^2 - 3x + 6$

  C $6x^5 + 2x^4 - 4x^3 + 9x^2 + 3x - 6$ D $6x^5 + 2x^4 - 4x^3 - 9x^2 - 3x + 6$

  E $6x^5 + 2x^4 - 4x^3 - 9x^2 + x - 2$

5 Which of the following is $(3x - 2)(x + 1) - x(1 - 2x)$?

  A $5x^2 - 2$ B $5x^2 - 3x - 1$ C $5x^2 + 2$

  D $3x^2 - 2x - 2$ E $x^2 - 2$

Exam-Style Question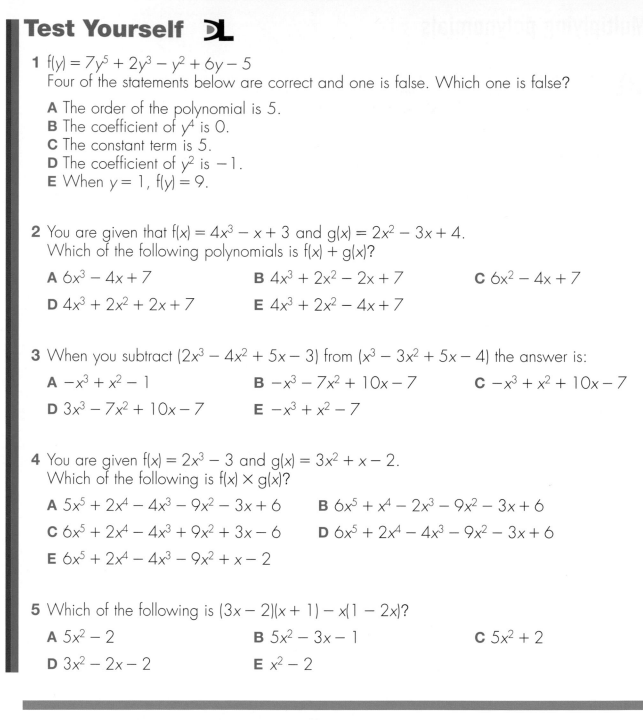

You are given that $f(x) = 5x^3 - 2x + 3$ and $g(x) = 2x^2 - 3x - 2$.

Find: i) $f(x) + g(x)$

        ii) $f(x) - g(x)$

        iii) $f(x) \times g(x)$

Polynomial division

A | ABOUT THIS TOPIC

As well as adding, subtracting and multiplying polynomials you also have to be able to divide one polynomial by another.

R | REMEMBER

- Long division using numbers from GCSE.
- Adding and subtracting polynomials from GCSE and C1.

K | KEY FACTS

- The words you use for dividing two whole numbers are important and you are going to use them in the next few topics.

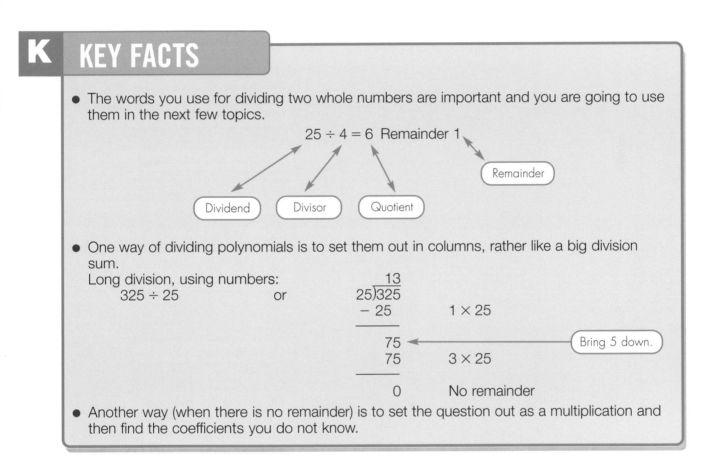

$$25 \div 4 = 6 \text{ Remainder } 1$$

Remainder

Dividend   Divisor   Quotient

- One way of dividing polynomials is to set them out in columns, rather like a big division sum.

  Long division, using numbers:

  $325 \div 25$ or

  $$\begin{array}{r} 13 \\ 25\overline{)325} \\ -25 \\ \hline 75 \\ 75 \\ \hline 0 \end{array}$$

  1×25

  3×25 Bring 5 down.

  No remainder

- Another way (when there is no remainder) is to set the question out as a multiplication and then find the coefficients you do not know.

3 POLYNOMIALS

EXAMPLE 1

Divide $2x^3 - 3x^2 + 6x - 5$ by $x - 1$ using columns.

SOLUTION

1. Lay it out in columns.

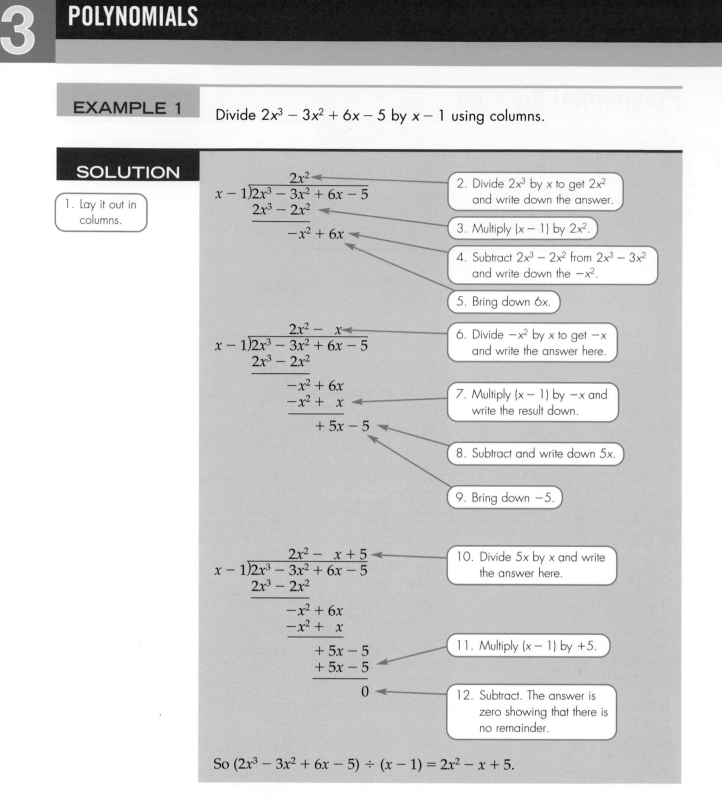

2. Divide $2x^3$ by x to get $2x^2$ and write down the answer.

3. Multiply $(x - 1)$ by $2x^2$.

4. Subtract $2x^3 - 2x^2$ from $2x^3 - 3x^2$ and write down the $-x^2$.

5. Bring down $6x$.

6. Divide $-x^2$ by x to get $-x$ and write the answer here.

7. Multiply $(x - 1)$ by $-x$ and write the result down.

8. Subtract and write down $5x$.

9. Bring down -5.

10. Divide $5x$ by x and write the answer here.

11. Multiply $(x - 1)$ by $+5$.

12. Subtract. The answer is zero showing that there is no remainder.

So $(2x^3 - 3x^2 + 6x - 5) \div (x - 1) = 2x^2 - x + 5$.

There is an alternative way of finding the quotient:

> ⚠ The method that follows is suitable only when the remainder is 0.

Divide $2x^3 - 3x^2 + 6x - 5$ by $x - 1$

Set this as $2x^3 - 3x^2 + 6x - 5 = (x - 1)($ $)$
and find what goes into the right bracket.

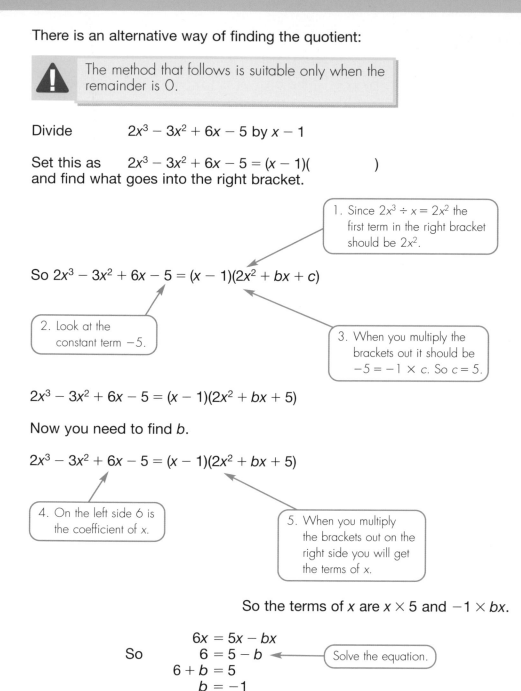

> 1. Since $2x^3 \div x = 2x^2$ the first term in the right bracket should be $2x^2$.

So $2x^3 - 3x^2 + 6x - 5 = (x - 1)(2x^2 + bx + c)$

> 2. Look at the constant term -5.

> 3. When you multiply the brackets out it should be $-5 = -1 \times c$. So $c = 5$.

$2x^3 - 3x^2 + 6x - 5 = (x - 1)(2x^2 + bx + 5)$

Now you need to find b.

$2x^3 - 3x^2 + 6x - 5 = (x - 1)(2x^2 + bx + 5)$

> 4. On the left side 6 is the coefficient of x.

> 5. When you multiply the brackets out on the right side you will get the terms of x.

So the terms of x are $x \times 5$ and $-1 \times bx$.

So
$$6x = 5x - bx$$
$$6 = 5 - b$$
$$6 + b = 5$$
$$b = -1$$

> Solve the equation.

$2x^3 - 3x^2 + 6x - 5 = (x - 1)(2x^2 - x + 5)$

Check the result by multiplying out the brackets on the right-hand side.

$$(x - 1)(2x^2 - x + 5)$$
$$= x(2x^2 - x + 5) - 1 \times (2x^2 - x + 5)$$
$$= 2x^3 - x^2 + 5x - 2x^2 + x - 5$$
$$= 2x^3 - 3x^2 + 6x - 5 \quad ✓$$

LINKS

Pure Mathematics   Sketching Curves (C1 and FP).

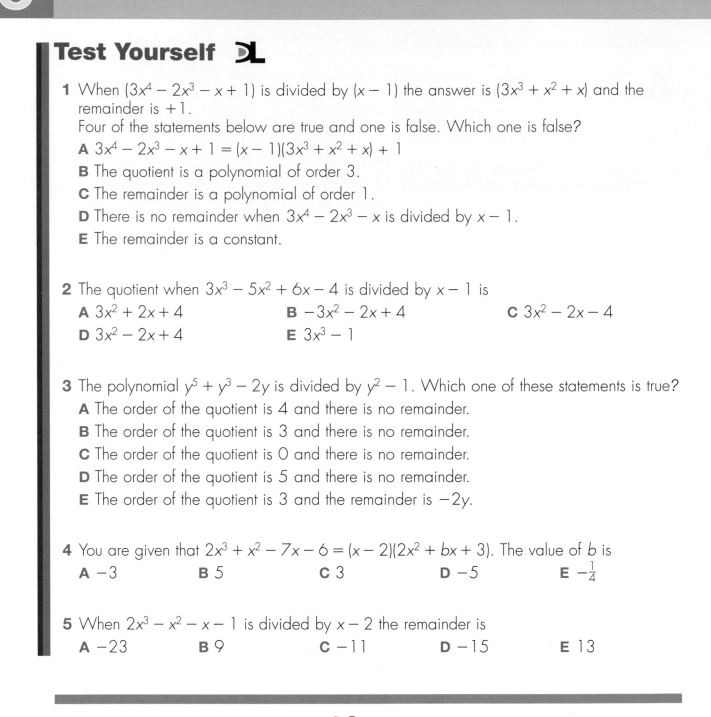

Test Yourself

1 When $(3x^4 - 2x^3 - x + 1)$ is divided by $(x - 1)$ the answer is $(3x^3 + x^2 + x)$ and the remainder is $+1$.
   Four of the statements below are true and one is false. Which one is false?
   A $3x^4 - 2x^3 - x + 1 = (x - 1)(3x^3 + x^2 + x) + 1$
   B The quotient is a polynomial of order 3.
   C The remainder is a polynomial of order 1.
   D There is no remainder when $3x^4 - 2x^3 - x$ is divided by $x - 1$.
   E The remainder is a constant.

2 The quotient when $3x^3 - 5x^2 + 6x - 4$ is divided by $x - 1$ is
   A $3x^2 + 2x + 4$ B $-3x^2 - 2x + 4$ C $3x^2 - 2x - 4$
   D $3x^2 - 2x + 4$ E $3x^3 - 1$

3 The polynomial $y^5 + y^3 - 2y$ is divided by $y^2 - 1$. Which one of these statements is true?
   A The order of the quotient is 4 and there is no remainder.
   B The order of the quotient is 3 and there is no remainder.
   C The order of the quotient is 0 and there is no remainder.
   D The order of the quotient is 5 and there is no remainder.
   E The order of the quotient is 3 and the remainder is $-2y$.

4 You are given that $2x^3 + x^2 - 7x - 6 = (x - 2)(2x^2 + bx + 3)$. The value of b is
   A -3 B 5 C 3 D -5 E $-\frac{1}{4}$

5 When $2x^3 - x^2 - x - 1$ is divided by $x - 2$ the remainder is
   A -23 B 9 C -11 D -15 E 13

Exam-Style Question

The polynomial $x^4 - 3x^2 + 3x + d$ is divisible by $(x + 1)$.
Divide $x^4 - 3x^2 + 3x + d$ by $(x + 1)$ and hence find the value of d.

Polynomial curves

You will often need to sketch the curve of a polynomial. The order of the polynomial and the sign of the highest power of the variable will give you important information about the shape of the curve.

- Graphs of quadratic functions from GCSE and C1.
- Previous work on polynomials from C1.

- Polynomial curves have turning points.

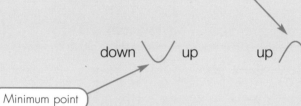

Maximum point

down ∨ up   up ∧ down

Minimum point

- The number of turning points depends on the order of a polynomial.

Order of polynomial	Number of turning points	Notes
1	0	Straight line
2	up to 1	Quadratic
3	up to 2	Cubic
4	up to 3	Quartic
⋮	⋮	
n	up to $(n-1)$	

- To sketch the curve of a polynomial you have to:
  i) Decide on the shape of the curve.
  ii) Show the turning points. Sometimes you will be asked to write the co-ordinates of the turning points.
  iii) Give the co-ordinates of the points where the curve crosses (intersects) the x axis and the y axis.
- To plot the curve of a polynomial you have to be more accurate. Calculate the values of y for suitable values of x, plot these points and join them as a smooth curve.
- Here are some examples of polynomials and their shapes:

Polynomial	Order	The coefficient of the highest power	Shape	
$3x - 4$	1	3 (positive)	/	up
$-2x + 3$	1	-2 (negative)	\	down
$2x^2 + x - 1$	2	2 (positive)	∨	up

Polynomial	Order	The coefficient of the highest power		Shape
$-3x^2 + 3x + 2$	2	-3 (negative)		down
$x^3 - x$	3	1 (positive)		up
$-x^3 - x^2$	3	-1 (negative)		down
$x^4 - 5x^2 + 4$	4	1 positive		up
$-x^4 + 5x^2 - 4$	4	-1 negative		down

EXAMPLE 1 Sketch the curve $y = x^3 - x = x(x - 1)(x + 1)$.

SOLUTION The polynomial is of order 3 (odd number) and the coefficient of x^3 is 1, which is a positive number. So expect the shape of the curve to be

Now find the points where the curve crosses the x axis and the y axis.
The curve crosses the x axis when $y = 0$.
Substitute $y = 0$ into $y = x^3 - x = x(x - 1)(x + 1)$
and solve the equation $\qquad x(x - 1)(x + 1) = 0$
So $\qquad\qquad\qquad x = 0$ or $x = 1$ or $x = -1$.

> **Note** that y co-ordinates are 0.

The curve crosses the x axis at the points $(-1, 0)$, $(0, 0)$ and $(1, 0)$.
The curve crosses the y axis when $x = 0$.
Substitute $x = 0$ into $y = x^3 - x = 0 - 0 = 0$.

> There are two turning points – a maximum point (max) and a minimum point (min).

> **⚠** Always remember to mark in the points of intersection with the *axes* when you are asked to sketch a curve.

> So the curve crosses the y axis at (0, 0).

> Points of intersection are shown.

EXAMPLE 2

Sketch the curve $y = -(x-1)(x-3)^2$.

SOLUTION

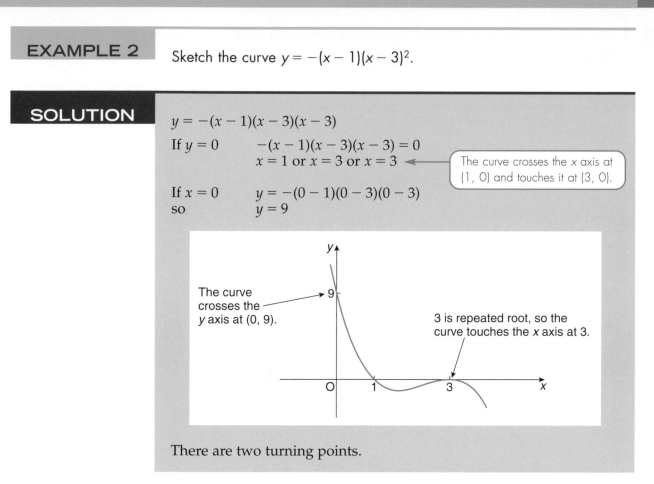

$y = -(x-1)(x-3)(x-3)$

If $y = 0$ $-(x-1)(x-3)(x-3) = 0$

$x = 1$ or $x = 3$ or $x = 3$ ←   The curve crosses the x axis at (1, 0) and touches it at (3, 0).

If $x = 0$ $y = -(0-1)(0-3)(0-3)$
so $y = 9$

The curve crosses the y axis at (0, 9).

3 is repeated root, so the curve touches the x axis at 3.

There are two turning points.

LINKS

Pure Mathematics	Solving Equations Graphically.
	Solving Inequalities.
	Sketching Curves.
Numerical Methods	Solving Equations Graphically.
Mechanics	Projectiles.
Further Pure Mathematics 1	Sketching Curves.

Test Yourself ▶L

1 Which of these is the graph of $y = mx + c$ when m is positive and c is negative?

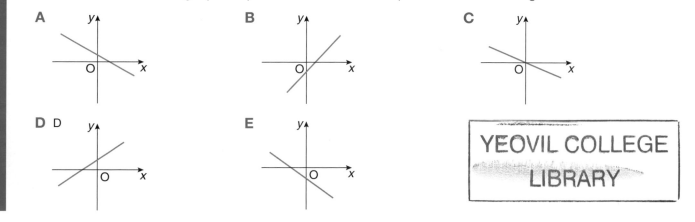

A   B   C

D D   E

2 For $y = (x - 3)^2(x + 2)^2(4 - x)$, four of the statements below are correct and one is false. Which one is false?

  A The polynomial is of order 5.

  B The curve of this polynomial touches the x axis at $(3, 0)$.

  C The coefficient of the highest power of x is negative.

  D The graph of the polynomial crosses the x axis at $(-4, 0)$.

  E The curve of this polynomial touches the x axis at $(-2, 0)$.

3 Which of the following graphs represents the shape of the curve $y = -x^3 + 3x + 3$?

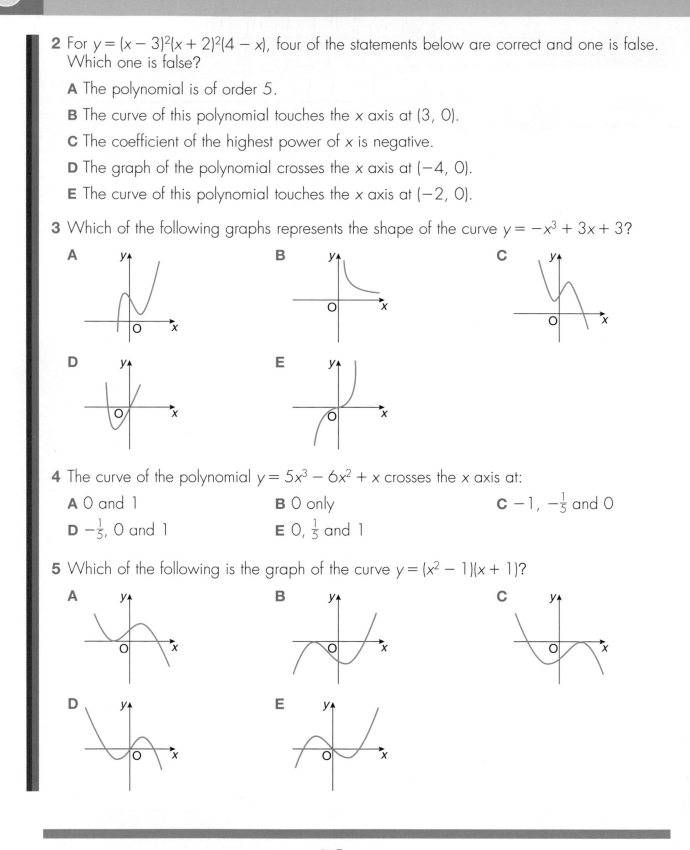

4 The curve of the polynomial $y = 5x^3 - 6x^2 + x$ crosses the x axis at:

  A 0 and 1   **B** 0 only   **C** -1, $-\frac{1}{5}$ and 0

  D $-\frac{1}{5}$, 0 and 1   **E** 0, $\frac{1}{5}$ and 1

5 Which of the following is the graph of the curve $y = (x^2 - 1)(x + 1)$?

Exam-Style Question ⅅL

You are given that $y = (3 - x)(x - 1)^2$.

i) Show that $y = -x^3 + 5x^2 - 7x + 3$.

ii) Sketch the graph of the polynomial.

The factor theorem

The factor theorem will help you to factorise polynomials easily, to solve equations and sketch polynomial curves.

- Substitution from GCSE.
- Factorising quadratic expressions from GCSE and C1.
- Solving equations from GCSE and C1.
- Division of polynomials from GCSE and C1.

The factor theorem says if $(x - a)$ is a factor of f(x) then f$(a) = 0$ and $x = a$ is a root of the equation f$(x) = 0$.

Conversely if f$(a) = 0$ then $(x - a)$ is a factor of f(x).

For example $\qquad$ f$(x) = 2x^3 + x^2 - 13x + 6$ is divisible by $x - 2$.
$\qquad\qquad$ So $\quad$ f$(2) = 2 \times 2^3 + 2^2 - 13 \times 2 + 6 = 0$.
Conversely, since f$(2) = 0$, $(x - 2)$ is a factor of f(x).

- To find the other factors of f(x) divide $2x^3 + x^2 - 13x + 6$ by $x - 2$.
  The quotient is a quadratic polynomial $2x^2 + 5x - 3$.

- Factorising $\qquad 2x^2 + 5x - 3$ gives $(2x - 1)(x + 3)$.
  So $\qquad\qquad 2x^3 + x^2 - 13x + 6 = (x - 2)(2x - 1)(x + 3)$
  and $\qquad\qquad (x - 2)$, $(2x - 1)$ and $(x + 3)$ are factors of the polynomial.

- The solution of the equation f$(x) = 2x^3 + x^2 - 13x + 6 = 0$
  $\qquad$ or $(x - 2)(2x - 1)(x + 3) = 0 \quad$ is $\quad x = 2$, $x = \frac{1}{2}$ or $x = -3$.

- The curve of f(x) crosses the x axis at $(2, 0)$, $(\frac{1}{2}, 0)$ and $(-3, 0)$.

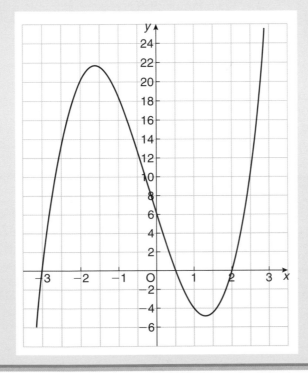

EXAMPLE 1

Show that $(x + 1)$ is a factor of $f(x) = x^3 + 2x^2 - 5x - 6$.

SOLUTION

Using the factor theorem
if $(x + 1)$ is a factor of $f(x)$ then $f(-1) = 0$.
$f(-1) = (-1)^3 + 2 \times (-1)^2 - 5 \times (-1) - 6$
$\quad = -1 + 2 + 5 - 6 = 0$
So $(x + 1)$ is a factor of $f(x) = x^3 + 2x^2 - 5x - 6$.

EXAMPLE 2

$f(x) = x^3 + 3x^2 - 4x - 12$
i) Find the values of $f(1)$, $f(-1)$, $f(2)$, $f(-2)$ and state two factors of the polynomial.
ii) Hence find two roots of the equation $x^3 + 3x^2 - 4x - 12 = 0$.
iii) Use the factor theorem to decide whether the third root is $x = 3$ or $x = -3$.

SOLUTION

i) $f(1) = 1^3 + 3 \times 1^2 - 4 \times 1 - 12 \qquad\qquad = -12$ $x - 1$ is not a factor.

$f(-1) = (-1)^3 + 3 \times (-1)^2 - 4 \times (-1) - 12 = -6$ $x + 1$ is not a factor.

$f(2) = 2^3 + 3 \times 2^2 - 4 \times 2 - 12 \qquad\quad = 0$ $x - 2$ is a factor.
$f(-2) = (-2)^3 + 3 \times (-2)^2 - 4 \times (-2) - 12 = 0$ $x + 2$ is a factor.
Since $\quad f(2) = 0 \qquad (x - 2)$ is a factor of $f(x)$.
$\qquad\quad f(-2) = 0 \quad (x + 2)$ is a factor of $f(x)$.

ii) $x = 2$ and $x = -2$ are roots of $f(x) = 0$.

iii) $x = 3 \qquad f(3) = 3^3 + 3 \times 3^2 - 4 \times 3 - 12 = 54 - 24 = 30 \qquad$ No
$x = -3 \qquad f(-3) = (-3)^3 + 3 \times (-3)^2 - 4 \times (-3) - 12 = 0 \qquad$ Yes
So $\qquad\quad x + 3$ is a factor of $f(x) = x^3 + 3x^2 - 4x - 12$.

EXAMPLE 3

You are given that $f(x) = x^3 - x^2 - 4x + 4$.
i) Factorise $x^3 - x^2 - 4x + 4$.
ii) Solve the equation $x^3 - x^2 - 4x + 4 = 0$.

> To find roots of the equation look at the constant term of the polynomial.

SOLUTION

$f(x) = x^3 - x^2 - 4x + 4$

The constant term is 4 and 4 is divisible by 1, -1, 2, -2, 4 and -4.
i) $f(1) \quad = 0 \qquad\qquad$ Yes $\qquad\qquad\qquad (x - 1)$ is a factor.
$f(-1) = 6 \qquad\qquad$ No
$f(2) \quad = 0 \qquad\qquad$ Yes $\qquad\qquad\qquad (x - 2)$ is a factor.
$f(-2) = 0 \qquad\qquad$ Yes $\qquad\qquad\qquad (x + 2)$ is a factor.
$f(4) \quad = 36 \qquad\quad$ No
$f(-4) = -60 \qquad\;$ No
$f(x) \quad = x^3 - x^2 - 4x + 4 = (x - 1)(x - 2)(x + 2)$
ii) The solution is $x = 1$, $x = 2$ or $x = -2$.

EXAMPLE 4

Given that $(x + 1)$ is a factor of $f(x) = x^3 - 3x^2 - x + 3$
i) factorise $x^3 - 3x^2 - x + 3$ completely
ii) solve the equation $x^3 - 3x^2 - x + 3 = 0$
iii) sketch the curve of $y = x^3 - 3x^2 - x + 3$.

SOLUTION

i) $(x + 1)$ is a factor of $f(x) = x^3 - 3x^2 - x + 3$.
To factorise completely you need to divide $x^3 - 3x^2 - x + 3$ by $(x + 1)$.

$$
\begin{array}{r}
x^2 - 4x + 3 \\
x + 1\overline{)x^3 - 3x^2 - \ x + 3}
\end{array}
$$

Subtract $x^3 + \ x^2$
_____

$-4x^2 - \ x$
Subtract $-4x^2 - 4x$
_____

$3x + 3$
Subtract $3x + 3$
_____
0

> Factorising $x^2 - 4x + 3$ gives $(x - 1)(x - 3)$.

A ADVICE

Factorise completely or factorise fully means keep going until there are no further factors to be found.

So $x^3 - 3x^2 - x + 3 = (x + 1)(x^2 - 4x + 3) = (x + 1)(x - 1)(x - 3)$.

ii) Solve $x^3 - 3x^2 - x + 3 = 0$ or $(x + 1)(x - 1)(x - 3) = 0$ means
either $(x + 1) = 0$ $x = -1$
or $(x - 1) = 0$ $x = 1$
or $(x - 3) = 0$ $x = 3$
So the solution of the equation is $x = -1, 1$ or 3.

iii) The curve $y = x^3 - 3x^2 - x + 3$ crosses the x axis at $(-1, 0)$, $(1, 0)$ and $(3, 0)$.

The curve crosses the y axis at $(0, 3)$.

LINKS

Pure Mathematics	Solving Equations.
	Sketching Curves.
Differential Equations	Solving Equations.
Mechanics	Kinematics (M1).

Test Yourself

1 $(x - 2)$ is a factor of one of these polynomials. Which one is it?

A $x^3 - 2x^2 - 3x + 1$ **B** $x^4 - 2x^3$ **C** $2x^3 - x^2 - 4$

D $x^2 + 4x - 16$ **E** $2x^3 - 4x^2 - 3x + 2$

2 $f(x) = 3x^3 - 2x^2 - 3x + 2$

Four of the statements below are true and one is false. Which one is false?

A $(x - 1)$ is a factor of the polynomial $f(x)$.

B When the polynomial $f(x)$ is divided by $(x + 1)$ there is no remainder.

C $(x + 2)$ is not a factor of the polynomial $f(x)$.

D For $x = -\frac{2}{3}$ $f(x) = 0$.

E There are three different values of x for which $f(x) = 0$.

3 A polynomial is given by $f(x) = x^3 - 3x^2 - 7x - 15$. Which one of these is a factor of $f(x)$?

A $(x - 1)$ **B** $(x - 3)$ **C** $(x - 5)$

D $(x + 1)$ **E** $(x + 3)$

4 A polynomial is given by $f(x) = x^4 + 2x^3 + 3x^2 + 4x + 2$.

Four of the following statements are false and one is true. Which one is true?

A The four roots of $f(x) = 0$ are $x = 1$, $x = -1$, $x = 2$ and $x = -2$.

B There are two different roots.

C The curve $y = f(x)$ touches the x axis.

D $(x + 1)$ is a factor of $f(x)$ but $(x + 1)^2$ is not a factor.

E $(x + 2)$ is a factor of $f(x)$.

5 Which of the following is the equation of the curve?

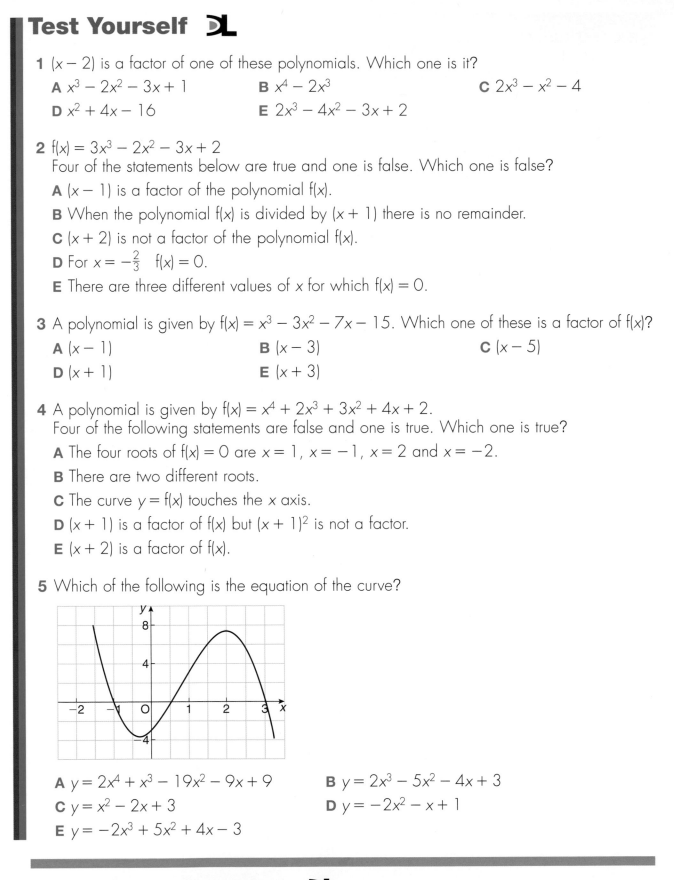

A $y = 2x^4 + x^3 - 19x^2 - 9x + 9$ **B** $y = 2x^3 - 5x^2 - 4x + 3$

C $y = x^2 - 2x + 3$ **D** $y = -2x^2 - x + 1$

E $y = -2x^3 + 5x^2 + 4x - 3$

Exam-Style Question

Given that $(x - 1)$ and $(x + 3)$ are factors of $x^3 - x^2 + ax + b$, find a and b.

The remainder theorem

A ABOUT THIS TOPIC

The remainder theorem is an extension of the factor theorem. The factor theorem covers cases when a linear expression like $(x - 3)$ divides exactly into a polynomial such as $f(x) = x^3 - 10x + 3$, that is, where the remainder is zero.

The remainder theorem covers cases when the linear expression does not divide exactly into a polynomial. It allows you to find the remainder without having to divide the polynomials.

R REMEMBER

- Division of polynomials from GCSE and C1.
- The factor theorem from C1.

K KEY FACTS

- The remainder theorem gives a quick way of finding the remainder.

  For example $f(1)$ is the remainder when $f(x)$ is divided by $(x - 1)$.
  $f(-2)$ is the remainder when $f(x)$ is divided by $(x + 2)$.

  In general, $f(a)$ is the remainder when $f(x)$ is divided by $(x - a)$.

- The remainder theorem is used only when the divisor is a linear expression.

Why the remainder theorem works

Look at $$f(x) = x^3 + 2x^2 - 3x - 4$$

This can be written as

$$f(x) = (x - 2)(x^2 + 4x + 5) + 6$$
so $$f(2) = (2 - 2)(x^2 + 4x + 5) + 6$$
$$= 0 \times (x^2 + 4x + 5) + 6 = 6$$

So the remainder when $x^3 + 2x^2 - 3x - 4$ is divided by $(x - 2)$ is 6 and $f(x)$ can be written as $(x - 2)(x^2 + 4x + 5) + 6$.

EXAMPLE 1

You are given that f(x) = x² − 4x + 5.
Find the remainder when f(x) is divided by (x − 4).

SOLUTION

When $x - 4 = 0$, $x = 4$.
So you want to find f(4) and this will be the remainder.

$f(4) = 4^2 - 4 \times 4 + 5 = 16 - 16 + 5 = 0 + 5 = 5$
The remainder when $f(x)$ is divided by $(x - 4)$ is 5.

EXAMPLE 2

You are given that f(x) = 2x³ − x² + x − 3.
Find the remainder when 2x³ − x² + x − 3 is divided by 2x − 1.

SOLUTION

When $2x - 1 = 0$, $x = \frac{1}{2}$.

So you want to find f$\left(\frac{1}{2}\right)$ and this will be the remainder.

$f(\frac{1}{2}) = 2 \times \left(\frac{1}{2}\right)^3 - \left(\frac{1}{2}\right)^2 + \left(\frac{1}{2}\right) - 3$

$= 2 \times \left(\frac{1}{8}\right) - \left(\frac{1}{4}\right) + \left(\frac{1}{2}\right) - 3$

$= \frac{1}{4} - \frac{1}{4} + \frac{1}{2} - \frac{3}{1}$

$= \frac{1}{2} - \frac{6}{2} = -\frac{5}{2} = -2.5$

The remainder when $2x^3 - x^2 + x - 3$ is divided by $(2x - 1)$ is −2.5.

EXAMPLE 3

When x³ + ax − 4x − 3 is divided by (x − 3) the remainder is 6. Find the value of a.

SOLUTION

The remainder when $f(x) = x^3 + ax - 4x - 3$ is divided by $(x - 3)$ is f(3).

$f(3) = 3^3 + a \times 3 - 4 \times 3 - 3$
$= 27 + 3a - 12 - 3$
$= 27 + 3a - 15$
$= 12 + 3a$

You are given that the remainder is 6.
So $12 + 3a = 6$
$3a = -12 + 6$
$3a = -6$
$a = -2$

To find a, solve the equation.

3

EXAMPLE 4

You are given that $f(x) = ax^2 + 3x + b$.

When $f(x)$ is divided by $(x - 1)$ the remainder is 7.
When $f(x)$ is divided by $(x - 2)$ the remainder is 13.
Find the values of a and b.

SOLUTION

There are two unknowns a and b, so two equations are needed.
When $ax^2 + 3x + b$ is divided by $(x - 1)$ the remainder is 7.
So $\qquad\qquad f(1) = 7$
$$a \times 1 + 3 + b = 7$$
$$a + b = 4 \qquad ①$$

When $ax^2 + 3x + b$ is divided by $(x - 2)$ the remainder is 13.
So $\qquad\qquad f(2) = 13$
$$a \times 2^2 + 3 \times 2 + b = 13$$
$$4a + 6 + b = 13$$
$$4a + b = 7 \qquad ②$$
Solving the simultaneous equations:
$$4a + b = 7 \qquad ②$$
$$a + b = 4 \qquad ①$$

②	$4a + b = 7$
①	$a + b = 4$

> Subtract equation ① from equation ② to eliminate b.

Subtract $\qquad\qquad 3a \quad\ = 3$
Giving $\qquad\qquad\ \ a \quad\ = 1$

Substitute $a = 1$ in the equation ①
$$a + b = 4$$
$$1 + b = 4$$
Taking 1 away from each side $\quad b = 3$

So the solution is $a = 1$ and $b = 3$

and $f(x) = x^2 + 3x + 3$.

LINKS

Pure Mathematics

The remainder theorem (C1) reinforces the factor theorem.

Test Yourself ⊃L

1 You are given that $f(x) = x^3 - 3x^2 + 6x - 18$.
Four of the statements below are true and one is false. Which one is false?

A The remainder when $x^3 - 3x^2 + 6x - 18$ is divided by $(x - 3)$ is 0.

B $(x + 1)$ is not a factor of $x^3 - 3x^2 + 6x - 18$.

C The remainder when $x^3 - 3x^2 + 6x - 18$ is divided by $(x + 2)$ is 0.

D The remainder when $x^3 - 3x^2 + 6x - 18$ is divided by $(x + 1)$ is -28.

E $(x - 3)$ is a factor of $x^3 - 3x^2 + 6x - 18$.

2 Find the remainder when $x^3 - 4x^2 + 5x - 3$ is divided by $x + 1$.

A -1	**B** -11	**C** -5
D -13	**E** -3	

3 When the polynomial $2y^4 + y^3 - y + 1$ is divided by $2y + 1$ the remainder is

A $\frac{3}{4}$	**B** $\frac{1}{2}$	**C** $\frac{3}{2}$	**D** $\frac{7}{4}$	**E** $\frac{5}{4}$

4 When $x^3 + 2x^2 + kx + 7$ is divided by $x + 1$ the remainder is 5. Find the value of k.

A 13	**B** 3	**C** 5
D -1	**E** -3	

5 When $ax^3 + bx^2 - 2x + 3$ is divided by $x - 2$ the remainder is 11 and when $ax^3 + bx^2 - 2x + 3$ is divided by $x + 1$ the remainder is 5. Find the values of a and b.

A $a = 3, b = -3$	**B** $a = 1, b = 1$	**C** $a = \frac{6}{5}, b = \frac{6}{5}$
D $a = \frac{1}{3}, b = \frac{11}{3}$	**E** $a = \frac{5}{6}, b = \frac{5}{6}$	

Exam-Style Question ⊃L

i) When $x^3 + kx + k^2$ is divided by $(x - 2)$ the remainder is 8. Find the non-zero value of k.

ii) Show that, with this value of k, $x + 2$ is a factor of $x^3 + kx + k^2$.

iii) Verify that $x^3 - 2x + 4$ can be written as $(x + 2)(x^2 - 2x + 2)$.

Quadratic graphs and their transformations

A | ABOUT THIS TOPIC

This topic is about techniques that can help when sketching quadratic and other functions.
The effects of transformations can help sketch a new function from an existing function. Completing the square finds the vertex and line of symmetry of a quadratic function. The quadratic equation formula is based on completing the square.

R | REMEMBER

- $(x + a)^2 = x^2 + 2ax + a^2$, $(x - a)^2 = x^2 - 2ax + a^2$ from GCSE.
- Translations expressed as $\begin{bmatrix} a \\ b \end{bmatrix}$ from GCSE.

K | KEY FACTS

- Transformations of functions: for any function $y = f(x)$
  - The graph of $y = f(x + a)$ is a translation of $-a$ units parallel to the x axis
  - The graph of $y = f(x) + b$ is a translation of b units parallel to the y axis.

  So $y = f(x + a) + b$ is a translation of $y = f(x)$ through $\begin{bmatrix} -a \\ b \end{bmatrix}$.

- Completing the square, for example with $y = x^2 + 10x + 12$
  - Halve the coefficient of the term in x and square the answer
  - Add it to the left two terms and subtract it from the right
  - Factorise the first three terms, to make a perfect square plus/minus something and tidy up.

  Half of 10 is 5

  $x^2 + 10x + 5^2 + 12 - 5^2$
  $(x + 5)^2 - 13$

- Using the completed square form of an equation to sketch the curves of quadratic functions, the graph of $y = a(x + p)^2 + q$ has a stationary point (or vertex) at $(-p, q)$.

Using transformations to sketch curves

EXAMPLE 1

Starting with the graph of $y = x^2$, sketch the graphs of
i) $y = (x - 4)^2$ **ii)** $y = x^2 - 5$ **iii)** $y = (x - 4)^2 - 5$.
In each case describe the transformation.

SOLUTION

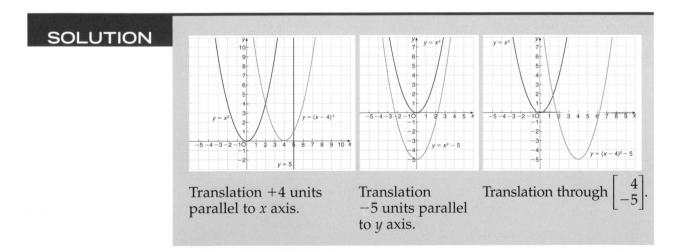

Translation $+4$ units parallel to x axis.

Translation -5 units parallel to y axis.

Translation through $\begin{bmatrix} 4 \\ -5 \end{bmatrix}$.

These transformations can be applied to any function.

EXAMPLE 2

The diagram shows the graph of $y = f(x)$.

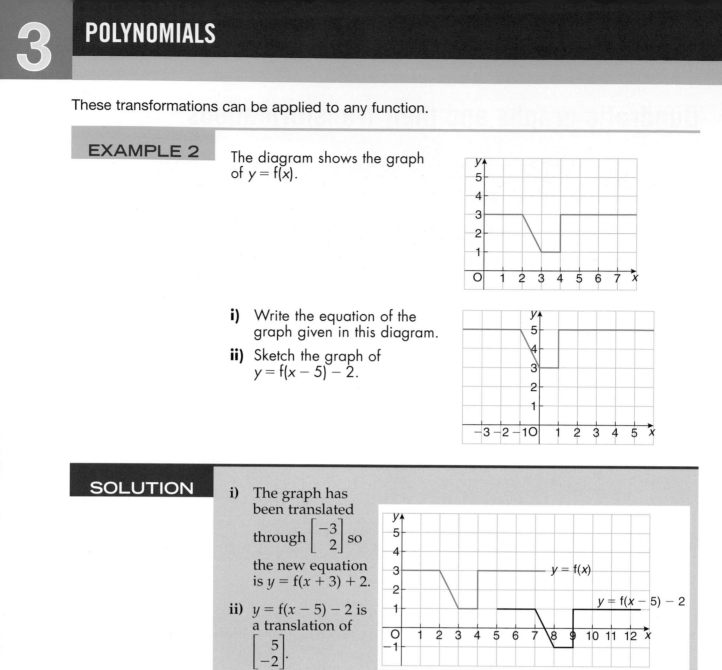

i) Write the equation of the graph given in this diagram.

ii) Sketch the graph of $y = f(x - 5) - 2$.

SOLUTION

i) The graph has been translated through $\begin{bmatrix} -3 \\ 2 \end{bmatrix}$ so the new equation is $y = f(x + 3) + 2$.

ii) $y = f(x - 5) - 2$ is a translation of $\begin{bmatrix} 5 \\ -2 \end{bmatrix}$.

$y = f(x)$

$y = f(x - 5) - 2$

Completing the square

EXAMPLE 3

Write $x^2 + 6x + 4$ in completed square form.

SOLUTION

Half of 6 is 3

$x^2 + 6x + 3^2 + 4 - 3^2$ Add 3^2 to the left and take it away from the right.

$\Rightarrow (x + 3)^2 + 4 - 9$ The terms $x^2 + 6x + 3^2$ make a perfect square.

$\Rightarrow (x + 3)^2 - 5$ Tidy up.

⚠️ When completing the square, the coefficient of x^2 must be 1. If it is not, you must first take out the coefficient of x^2 as a factor.

EXAMPLE 4

Write $2x^2 - 12x + 6 = 0$ in completed square form.

SOLUTION

$2x^2 - 16x + 6$

$= 2(x^2 - 8x) + 6$ — Take 2 out as a factor of the two left-hand terms.

$= 2(x^2 - 8x) + 4^2 \times 2 + 6 - 4^2 \times 2$ — Add $4^2 \times 2$ to the left and take it away from the right.

$= 2(x^2 - 8x + 4^2) + 6 - 16 \times 2$ — The 4^2 can now be put inside the bracket.

$= 2(x - 4)^2 + 3 - 32$ — Factorise $x^2 - 8x + 4^2$.

$= 2(x - 4)^2 - 29$ — Tidy up.

Graphs of quadratic functions

Completing the square tells you a lot about the position of the graph.

The graph of $y = (x + p)^2 + q$ has a stationary point (or vertex) at $(-p, q)$.

Notice that the curve is symmetrical about the stationary point so the line $x = -p$ is a line of symmetry.

EXAMPLE 5

Sketch the curve $y = x^2 + 6x + 4$.

SOLUTION

In example 3 it was shown that the equation can be written as $y = (x + 3)^2 - 5$, so the minimum point is at $(-3, -5)$ and the line of symmetry is $x = -3$.

From the equation it can be seen that the curve cuts the y axis at $(0, 4)$.

⚠️ A curve with a negative coefficient for x^2 is upside down (i.e., n-shaped rather than u-shaped).

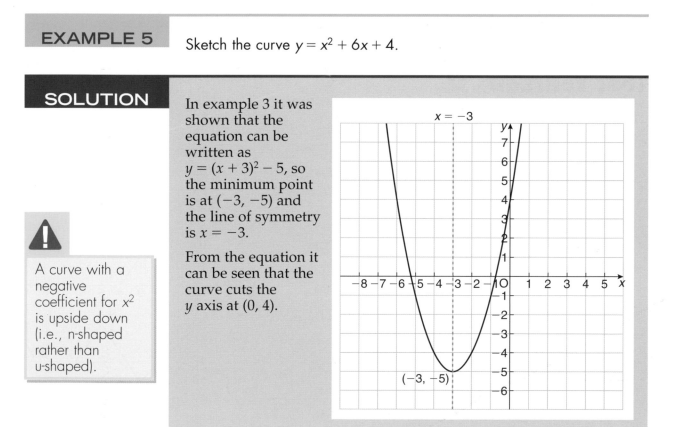

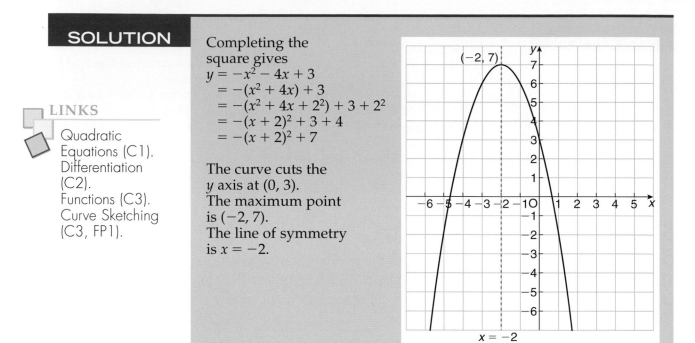

EXAMPLE 6

Use completing the square to sketch the curve $y = -x^2 - 4x + 3$.

SOLUTION

Completing the square gives
$$y = -x^2 - 4x + 3$$
$$= -(x^2 + 4x) + 3$$
$$= -(x^2 + 4x + 2^2) + 3 + 2^2$$
$$= -(x + 2)^2 + 3 + 4$$
$$= -(x + 2)^2 + 7$$

The curve cuts the y axis at $(0, 3)$.
The maximum point is $(-2, 7)$.
The line of symmetry is $x = -2$.

LINKS

Quadratic
Equations (C1).
Differentiation (C2).
Functions (C3).
Curve Sketching (C3, FP1).

Test Yourself ▶L

1 The diagram shows the graph of $y = g(x)$ and its image $y = h(x)$ after a translation. The equation of the image is

A $y = g(x + 3) - 5$
B $y = g(x - 3) + 5$
C $y = g(x - 3) - 5$
D $y = g(x + 3) + 5$
E $y = g(x + 5) + 3$

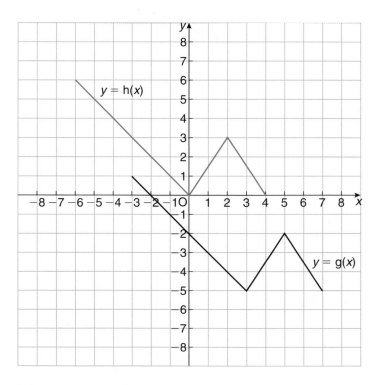

2 The curve $y = x^2 - 4x$ is translated and the equation of the new curve is $y = (x - 1)^2 - 4(x - 1) + 2$. What are the co-ordinates of the vertex of the new curve?
  A $(1, 2)$ **B** $(1, -2)$ **C** $(3, -2)$ **D** $(1, 5)$ **E** $(1, -6)$

3 The curve $y = x^2 - 2x + 3$ is translated through $\begin{bmatrix} 2 \\ -4 \end{bmatrix}$. Find the equation of the new curve.

A $y = x^2 + 2x - 1$ **B** $y = x^2 - 6x + 11$ **C** $y = x^2 - 6x + 15$

D $y = 4x^2 - 4x - 1$ **E** $y = x^2 - 6x + 7$

4 Write $x^2 - 12x + 3$ in completed square form.

A $(x - 6)^2 + 3$ **B** $(x - 12)^2 - 141$ **C** $(x + 6)^2 - 33$

D $(x - 6 - \sqrt{33})(x - 6 + \sqrt{33})$ **E** $(x - 6)^2 - 33$

5 Using the co-ordinates of the turning point and the equation of the line of symmetry state which one of the following is the equation of this curve.

A $y = (x - 3)^2 - 4$ **B** $y = (x - 3)^2 + 4$

C $y = (x + 3)^2 + 4$ **D** $y = (x + 4)^2 - 3$

E $y = (x + 3)^2 - 4$

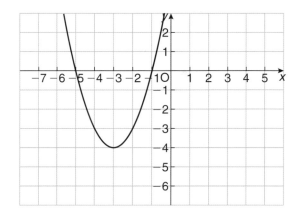

Exam-Style Question

You are given that $f(x) = x^2 - 6x + 4$.

i) Express $f(x)$ in the form $(x + p)^2 + q$ where p and q are integers.

ii) The curve C with equation $y = f(x)$ meets the y axis at P and has a minimum point at Q. State the co-ordinates of P and Q and sketch the curve.

iii) The curve C is translated by 1 unit parallel to the x axis and -2 units parallel to the y axis. State the co-ordinates of Q′, the image of Q after the translation and write down the equation of the new curve.

Binomial theorem and expansions

A ABOUT THIS TOPIC

A binomial expression is one with two parts such as $(1 + x)$. When a binomial expression is raised to a power, the resulting polynomial is called a binomial expansion. Binomial expansions are widely used throughout mathematics so this is the start of an important topic.

R REMEMBER

- Expanding brackets from GCSE.

K KEY FACTS

- The binomial expansion of $(ax + by)^n$ is
  $$(ax + by)^n = {}^nC_0(ax)^n + {}^nC_1(ax)^{n-1}(by)^1 + {}^nC_2x^{n-2}y^2 + {}^nC_3(ax)^{n-3}(by)^3 + \ldots + {}^nC_n(by)^n$$
- Binomial coefficients can be found by
  - using Pascal's triangle
  - using the formula ${}^nC_r = \frac{n!}{r!(n-r)!}$
- $\binom{n}{r}$ is another way of writing ${}^nC_r$.

Expanding brackets

These are binomial expressions. →
$$(x + a)^2 = x^2 + 2ax + a^2$$
$$(x + a)^3 = x^3 + 3ax^2 + 3a^2x + a^3$$
$$(x + a)^4 = x^4 + 4ax^3 + 6a^2x^2 + 4a^3x + a^4$$

Polynomials produced by expanding brackets in this way are called binomial expansions.

Notice that there are two things to think about in these binomial expansions:

- The powers of the terms in x reduce by one each term and the powers of a increase by one each term. The sum of the two powers is always the same as the power of the bracket.
- The coefficients of the terms. One way of finding them is to use Pascal's triangle.

Pascal's triangle

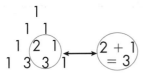

Each number in Pascal's triangle is found by adding the two above it as you can see in the diagram. The numbers are the same as the coefficients in the expansions shown in the previous 'Expanding brackets' paragraph.

You can use Pascal's triangle to help you write out binomial expansions.

A ADVICE

Notice that the entries in each row are symmetrical about the middle number.

EXAMPLE 1

Write out the binomial expansion of $(3a + 2b)^4$.

SOLUTION

The binomial coefficients for the fourth row of Pascal's triangle are 1, 4, 6, 4, 1. Thus

$$(3a + 2b)^4 = 1(3a)^4 + 4(3a)^3(2b)^1 + 6(3a)^2(2b)^2 + 4(3a)^1(2b)^3 + (2b)^4$$
$$= 81a^4 + 4 \times 27a^3 \times 2b + 6 \times 9a^2 \times 4b^2 + 4 \times 3a \times 8b^3 + 16b^4$$
$$= 81a^4 + 216a^3b + 216a^2b^2 + 96ab^3 + 16b^4.$$

EXAMPLE 2

Write out the binomial expansion of $(x - 2)^3$

SOLUTION

The binomial coefficients for the third row of Pascal's triangle are 1, 3, 3, 1.
So you get $(x - 2)^3 = 1x^3 + 3x^2(-2)^1 + 3x^1(-2)^2 + 1(-2)^3$
$$= x^3 - 6x^2 + 12x - 8.$$

> ⚠ Notice that the negative sign in front of the 2 is treated as part of the number: $x - 2 = x + (-2)$.
> The end result gives you alternating plus and minus signs in the expansion.

Factorials

The quantity 4 factorial is written 4! and is defined as $4! = 4 \times 3 \times 2 \times 1$.

EXAMPLE 3

What is the value of 7!?

> There is a button on your calculator that will calculate these values.

SOLUTION

$7! = 7 \times 6 \times 5 \times 4 \times 3 \times 2 \times 1 = 5040$

A

ADVICE

Remember that $0! = 1$.

Binomial coefficients

Since there is a pattern to the binomial coefficients, there is a formula for calculating them.

Think about $(a + b)^4 = a^4 + 4a^3b + 6a^2b^2 + 4ab^3 + b^4$.

The coefficients are summarised in this table where n is the power of the bracket and r is the power of b.

The binomial coefficient for any value of n and r can be written ^nC_r or $\binom{n}{r}$.

$n = 4$ r	0	1	2	3	4
Coefficients	1	4	6	4	1

The formula for calculating this value is $^nC_r = \dfrac{n!}{r!(n - r)!}$.

EXAMPLE 4

Use the formula $^nC_r = \dfrac{n!}{r!(n-r)!}$ to calculate $^8C_3$.

SOLUTION

$$^8C_3 = \frac{8!}{3!(8-3)!} = \frac{8!}{3! \times 5!} = \frac{40\,320}{6 \times 120} = 56$$

The binomial theorem

Using the formula $^nC_r = \dfrac{n!}{r!(n-r)!}$ it is possible to write a binomial expansion even if you cannot remember Pascal's triangle. So

$$(a+b)^4 = \frac{4!}{4!0!}a^4b^0 + \frac{4!}{3!1!}a^3b^1 + \frac{4!}{2!2!}a^2b^2 + \frac{4!}{1!3!}a^1b^3 + \frac{4!}{0!4!}a^0b^4$$

$$= a^4 + 4a^3b + 6a^2b^2 + 4ab^3 + b^4.$$

> **A ADVICE**
>
> In the expansion of $(a + bx)^n$ there will be $n + 1$ terms.
> Also notice that the sum of the powers of a and b is always the same as the power of the bracket.

EXAMPLE 5

Write in full the expansion of $(1 + x)^4$.

SOLUTION

$$(1 + x)^4 = {}^4C_0\,1^4x^0 + {}^4C_1\,1^3x^1 + {}^4C_2\,1^2x^2 + {}^4C_3\,1^1x^3 + {}^4C_4\,1^0x^4$$

$$= \frac{4!}{4!0!}1^4x^0 + \frac{4!}{3!1!}1^3x^1 + \frac{4!}{2!2!}1^2x^2 + \frac{4!}{1!3!}1^1x^3 + \frac{4!}{0!4!}1^0x^4$$

$$= 1 + 4x + 6x^2 + 4x^3 + x^4$$

> Notice that $^nC_0 = {}^nC_n = 1$.

In general the binomial expansion of $(x + y)^n$ can be written

$$(x+y)^n = {}^nC_0x^n + {}^nC_1x^{n-1}y^1 + {}^nC_2x^{n-2}y^2 + {}^nC_3x^{n-3}y^3 + \ldots + {}^nC_ny^n$$

or $(x+y)^n = \displaystyle\sum_{r=0}^{n} {}^nC_r x^{n-r}y^r$ where n is a positive integer.

You can also use the formula $^nC_r = \dfrac{n!}{r!(n-r)!}$ to calculate single terms in a binomial expansion.

EXAMPLE 6

What is the term in x^4 in the expansion $(2 + 3x)^6$?

SOLUTION

The term will be

$$^6C_4(2)^2(3x)^4 = \frac{6!}{4!(6-4)!}(2)^2(3x)^4$$

$$= \frac{{}^3\cancel{6} \times 5 \times \cancel{4} \times \cancel{3} \times \cancel{2} \times \cancel{1}}{\cancel{4} \times \cancel{3} \times \cancel{2} \times 1 \times \cancel{2} \times \cancel{1}}(2)^2(3x)^4$$

$$= 3 \times 5 \times (2)^2(3x)^4 = 4860x^4.$$

> 4, 3, 2, 1 have been cancelled and the 6 on the top has been cancelled with the remaining 2 on the bottom (denominator).

EXAMPLE 7

i) Write out the binomial expansion of $(1 + 2x)^4$.
ii) Use the first three terms in the expansion to calculate an approximate value of 1.02^4. Give your answer to 4 significant figures.

SOLUTION

i) $(1 + 2x)^4 = {}^4C_0 + {}^4C_1(2x) + {}^4C_2(2x)^2 + {}^4C_3(2x)^3 + {}^4C_4(2x)^4$
$= 1 + 8x + 24x^2 + 32x^3 + 16x^4$

ii) Notice that for $x = 0.01$, $(1 + 2x) = 1.02$ so you can write
$(1 + 2x)^4 \equiv 1.02^4 = (1 + 0.02)^4$.

Substitute this value for x into the expansion you have found.

$1.02^4 = (1 + 0.02)^4 = 1 + 8(0.01) + 24(0.01)^2$
$= 1 + 0.08 + 0.0024$
$= 1.0824$
$= 1.082 \text{ (4 s.f.)}$

LINKS

Pure Mathematics
Statistics 1

Approximations (C4).
Selections (S1).
Binomial Probability Distribution (S1).
Hypothesis Testing (S1).

Test Yourself ▷L

1 Without using a calculator, find the value of ${}^{12}C_8$.

   A 11 880   B 495   C 19 958 400   D 2970   E 1680

2 Simplify $(x - 1)^3 + (x + 1)^3$.

   A $2x^3 + 6x$ B $2x^3$ C $2x^3 + 2x$ D $2x^3 + 6x^2 + 6x + 2$ E $8x^3$

3 Find the coefficient of x^5 in the expansion of $(2 - x)^8$.

   A $-{}^8C_5$ B $-{}^8C_5 \times 2^5$ C ${}^8C_5 \times 2^3$ D $-{}^8C_5 \times 2^3$ E $-{}^8C_3 \times 2^5$

4 Write out the binomial expansion of $(1 - 3x)^4$.

   A $1 + 12x + 54x^2 + 108x^3 + 81x^4$ B $1 - 12x + 54x^2 - 108x^3 + 81x^4$

   C $1 - 12x - 18x^2 - 12x^3 - 3x^4$ D $1 - 12x + 108x^2 - 684x^3 + 1944x^4$

   E $1 - 3x + 9x^2 - 27x^3 + 81x^4$

5 Jo knows the binomial expansion of $(1 + 6x)^{10}$. She wants to use it to obtain an approximation for 0.97^{10}. What should she take as a value for x?

   A 0.01   B 0.005   C −0.005   D −0.03   E −0.05

Exam-Style Question ▷L

a) i) Expand $(1 - 2x)^{10}$ as far as the term in x^4.
   ii) Use your expansion to find 0.98^{10} correct to three decimal places.
b) Find the coefficient of x^4 in the expansion $(1 + 5x)(1 - 2x)^{10}$.

Uncertainty

4

Inequalities

A ABOUT THIS TOPIC

Inequalities are very useful for expressing ranges of values. The algebra of inequalities is very similar to the algebra of equations, but there are a couple of small, yet important, differences.

R REMEMBER

- Equation of a line from GCSE and C1.
- Quadratic equations from GCSE and C1.
- Solving linear and quadratic equations from GCSE and C1.
- Graphs of quadratic equations from GCSE and C1.

K KEY FACTS

- Solving linear inequalities is very similar to solving linear equations; however you should bear in mind the following:
  - When swapping the sides of an inequality you should reverse the direction of the inequality sign
  - When multiplying or dividing both sides of an inequality by a negative number you should reverse the direction of the inequality. It is often best to avoid multiplying or dividing by a negative number if you can.
- To solve a quadratic inequality you should solve the corresponding quadratic equation and then use a graph to determine the solution to the inequality.

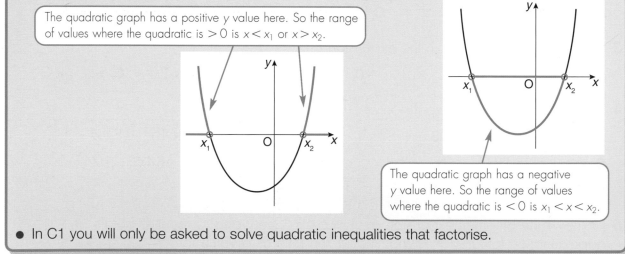

The quadratic graph has a positive y value here. So the range of values where the quadratic is > 0 is $x < x_1$ or $x > x_2$.

The quadratic graph has a negative y value here. So the range of values where the quadratic is < 0 is $x_1 < x < x_2$.

- In C1 you will only be asked to solve quadratic inequalities that factorise.

Linear inequalities

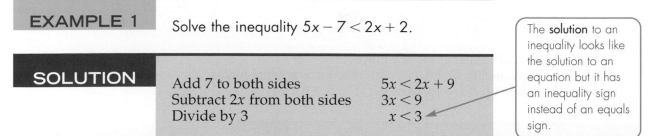

EXAMPLE 1   Solve the inequality $5x - 7 < 2x + 2$.

SOLUTION

Add 7 to both sides	$5x < 2x + 9$
Subtract $2x$ from both sides	$3x < 9$
Divide by 3	$x < 3$

The **solution** to an inequality looks like the solution to an equation but it has an inequality sign instead of an equals sign.

If you multiply or divide both sides of an inequality by a negative number you should reverse the direction of the inequality, but this can usually be avoided. Look at the next example to see how.

EXAMPLE 2

Solve the inequality $4 - 3x \geqslant 6 - x$.

SOLUTION

Method 1 – dividing by a negative number

Solve the inequality	$4 - 3x \geqslant 6 - x$
Add x to both sides	$4 - 2x \geqslant 6$
Subtract 4 from both sides	$-2x \geqslant 2$
Divide both sides by -2	$x \leqslant -1$

> Dividing by a negative number reverses the direction of the inequality sign.

SOLUTION

Method 2 – simpler method that avoids dividing by a negative number

Solve the inequality	$4 - 3x \geqslant 6 - x$
Add $3x$ to both sides	$4 \geqslant 6 + 2x$
Subtract 6 from both sides	$-2 \geqslant 2x$
Divide both sides by 2	$-1 \geqslant x$
Rewrite with x the subject	$x \leqslant -1$

A ADVICE

Inequalities should be written with x as the subject. You can do this here by changing the sides but this will mean changing the direction of the inequality from $\geqslant$ to $\leqslant$. Notice that '-1 is greater than or equal to x' means the same as 'x is less than or equal to -1'.

EXAMPLE 3

Solve the inequality $\dfrac{x - 4}{2} < \dfrac{4 - x}{3}$.

SOLUTION

> 6 is the lowest common multiple of 2 and 3.

Multiply by 6	$3(x - 4) < 2(4 - x)$
Expand	$3x - 12 < 8 - 2x$
Add $2x$ to both sides	$5x - 12 < 8$
Add 12 to both sides	$5x < 20$
Divide both sides by 5	$x < 4$

EXAMPLE 4

Sketch the lines $y = 3x + 1$ and $y = -2x - 4$. For what values of x is the line $y = 3x + 1$ above the line $y = -2x - 4$?

Test Yourself ▷L

1 Solve $x + 7 < 3x - 5$.

   A $x > 6$ **B** $x > 1$ **C** $x < 1$ **D** $x < 6$ **E** $x > 4$

2 Solve $\dfrac{2(2x + 1)}{3} \geq 6$.

   A $x \geq 5$ **B** $x \geq \frac{3}{2}$ **C** $x > 4$ **D** $x \geq 4$ **E** $x > 5$

3 The graph shows the lines $y = 3x - 3$ and $y = -x + 5$.
For what values of x is the line $y = 3x - 3$ above the line
$y = -x + 5$?

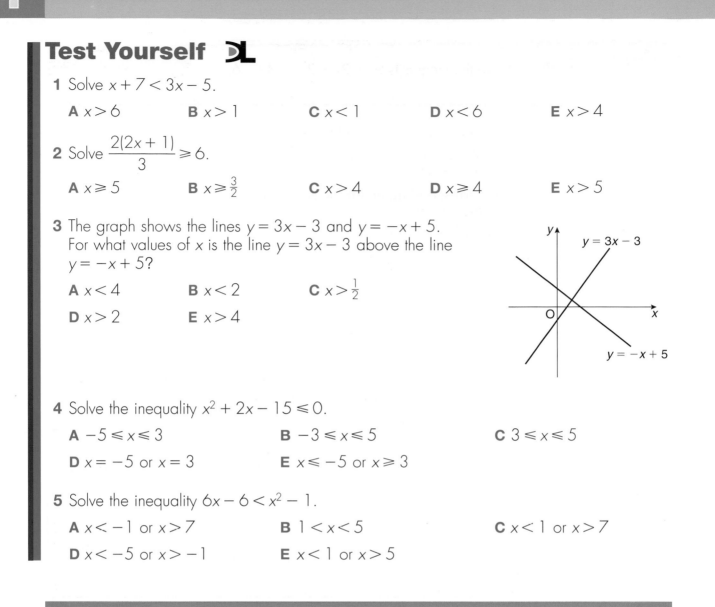

   A $x < 4$ **B** $x < 2$ **C** $x > \frac{1}{2}$

   D $x > 2$ **E** $x > 4$

4 Solve the inequality $x^2 + 2x - 15 \leq 0$.

   A $-5 \leq x \leq 3$ **B** $-3 \leq x \leq 5$ **C** $3 \leq x \leq 5$

   D $x = -5$ or $x = 3$ **E** $x \leq -5$ or $x \geq 3$

5 Solve the inequality $6x - 6 < x^2 - 1$.

   A $x < -1$ or $x > 7$ **B** $1 < x < 5$ **C** $x < 1$ or $x > 7$

   D $x < -5$ or $x > -1$ **E** $x < 1$ or $x > 5$

Exam-Style Question ▷L

i)   Solve the inequality $\dfrac{2(3x - 4)}{5} \leq -4$.

ii)   Solve the inequality $x^2 - x - 2 > 4$.

INDICES

5

Surds and indices

A · ABOUT THIS TOPIC

This topic builds on your knowledge of indices from GCSE. After studying this you will be able to manipulate and simplify numerical and algebraic expressions which contain indices.

Indices is the plural of index; index is another word for power.

Questions on indices are usually expected to be done without a calculator and so they frequently occur on non-calculator papers.

R · REMEMBER

- Laws of indices from GCSE.

K · KEY FACTS

- A surd is an expression containing an irrational root, such as $5 + \sqrt{3}$ or $2 - \sqrt[3]{7}$.
- In the expression a^m, a is the base and m is the index or power to which the base is raised.

R · RULE

Laws of indices

Multiplication	$a^m \times a^n = a^{m+n}$
Division	$\dfrac{a^m}{a^n} = a^{m-n}$
Power of a power	$(a^m)^n = a^{mn}$

Negative and fractional indices

$$a^{-m} = \frac{1}{a^m}$$

$$a^{\frac{1}{m}} = \sqrt[m]{a}$$

Surds

Surds are used when an exact answer is required. Surds can be simplified, added and subtracted in the same way as algebraic expressions, keeping the rational numbers and square roots separate.

EXAMPLE 1

Simplify   **i)** $\sqrt{32}$ **ii)** $4\sqrt{3} + 3\sqrt{3}$ **iii)** $(4 + 2\sqrt{11}) + (5 - 6\sqrt{11})$.

SOLUTION

i) $\sqrt{32} = \sqrt{16 \times 2} = \sqrt{16} \times \sqrt{2} = 4\sqrt{2}$

ii) $4\sqrt{3} + 3\sqrt{3} = 7\sqrt{3}$

iii) $(4 + 2\sqrt{11}) + (5 - 6\sqrt{11}) = 9 - 4\sqrt{11}$

EXAMPLE 2

Simplify $(3 + 3\sqrt{7})(2 - 4\sqrt{7})$.

SOLUTION

$(3 + 3\sqrt{7}) \times (2 - 4\sqrt{7})$
$= (3 \times 2) + (3 \times -4\sqrt{7}) + (3\sqrt{7} \times 2) + (3\sqrt{7} \times -4\sqrt{7})$
$= 6 - 12\sqrt{7} + 6\sqrt{7} + (-12 \times 7)$
$= -78 - 6\sqrt{7}$

EXAMPLE 3

Simplify $\dfrac{5}{\sqrt{3}}$.

SOLUTION

$\dfrac{5}{\sqrt{3}} = \dfrac{5}{\sqrt{3}} \times \dfrac{\sqrt{3}}{\sqrt{3}} = \dfrac{5\sqrt{3}}{3}$.

> Multiplying by $\sqrt{3}$ here makes the bottom line into a whole number.
> You must also multiply the top by $\sqrt{3}$.

EXAMPLE 4

Simplify $\dfrac{5 - 2\sqrt{3}}{4 + 2\sqrt{3}}$.

SOLUTION

$\dfrac{5 - 2\sqrt{3}}{4 + 2\sqrt{3}}$

$= \dfrac{5 - 2\sqrt{3}}{4 + 2\sqrt{3}} \times \dfrac{4 - 2\sqrt{3}}{4 - 2\sqrt{3}}$

$= \dfrac{20 - 10\sqrt{3} - 8\sqrt{3} + 12}{16 - 12}$

$= \dfrac{32 - 18\sqrt{3}}{4} = \dfrac{16 - 9\sqrt{3}}{2}$

A ADVICE

Multiply top and bottom by $4 - 2\sqrt{3}$ because this will make the bottom a whole number.
If you multiply top and bottom by the same thing, you are really multiplying by 1 and so you are not changing the value of the expression.

Indices

> ⚠ Remember that any non-zero number to the power zero is equal to one:
> $5^0 = 1$, $(-3)^0 = 1$, $1.7^0 = 1$, $a^0 = 1$.

R RULE

Laws of indices

$a^m \times a^n = a^{m+n}$ $\dfrac{a^m}{a^n} = a^{m-n}$ $(a^m)^n = a^{mn}$

EXAMPLE 5

Simplify **i)** $3a^5 \times 4a^2$ **ii)** $\dfrac{39x^4}{13x^3}$ **iii)** $(5y^4)^2$.

SOLUTION

i) $3a^5 \times 4a^2 = 3 \times 4 \times a^5 \times a^2 = 12a^{5+2} = 12a^7$

ii) $\dfrac{39x^4}{13x^3} = \dfrac{39}{13} \times \dfrac{x^4}{x^3} = 3x^{4-3} = 3x$

iii) $(5y^4)^2 = 5^2 \times (y^4)^2 = 25y^{4\times2} = 25y^8$

Negative and fractional indices

Negative and fractional powers like $a^{\frac{1}{2}}$ and a^{-4} obey the laws of indices in the same way as positive integer powers such as a^3.

A negative index indicates a reciprocal $a^{-m} = \dfrac{1}{a^m}$.

A fractional index is a root $a^{\frac{1}{m}} = \sqrt[m]{a}$.

| EXAMPLE 6 | Simplify $27^{\frac{2}{3}}$. |

| SOLUTION | $27^{\frac{2}{3}} = \left(27^{\frac{1}{3}}\right)^2 = 3^2 = 9$ |

> It is also possible to do this calculation like this
> $27^{\frac{2}{3}} = (27^2)^{\frac{1}{3}} = 729^{\frac{1}{3}} = 9$
> but this would be harder to work out.

| EXAMPLE 7 | Write $\dfrac{1}{81}$ as the base 3 raised to a power. |

| SOLUTION | $81 = 3^4$
$\dfrac{1}{81} = \dfrac{1}{3^4} = 3^{-4}$ |

| EXAMPLE 8 | Write $625^{\frac{1}{4}}$ as a whole number. |

| SOLUTION | $625^{\frac{1}{4}} = \sqrt[4]{625} = 5$ |

| EXAMPLE 9 | Solve the equation $x^{\frac{1}{3}} = -4$. |

| SOLUTION | $x^{\frac{1}{3}} = \sqrt[3]{x}$ so $\sqrt[3]{x} = -4$ $x = (-4)^3 = -64$ |

Mixed bases

If a question involves using more than one base, you can split them up using the rule $(a \times b)^n = a^n \times b^n$. This can help to simplify the solution to more complicated problems.

| EXAMPLE 10 | Simplify $2a^3b^2 \times 4a^2b^4$. |

| SOLUTION | $2a^3b^2 \times 4a^2b^4 = 2 \times 4 \times a^3 \times a^2 \times b^2 \times b^4 = 8a^5b^6$ |

EXAMPLE 11

Simplify $\dfrac{\left(36^2 \times \frac{1}{2^3} \times \sqrt{3}\right)^4}{6^3}$.

SOLUTION

First notice that $36 = 4 \times 9 = 2^2 \times 3^2$ and also that $6 = 2 \times 3$.

Substituting into the expression gives

$$\frac{[(2^2 \times 3^2)^2 \times 2^{-3} \times 3^{\frac{1}{2}}]^4}{(2 \times 3)^3} = \frac{[2^4 \times 3^4 \times 2^{-3} \times 3^{\frac{1}{2}}]^4}{2^3 \times 3^3}$$

$$= \frac{[2^{4-3} \times 3^{4+\frac{1}{2}}]^4}{2^3 \times 3^3} = \frac{[2 \times 3^{\frac{9}{2}}]^4}{2^3 \times 3^3} = \frac{2^4 \times 3^{18}}{2^3 \times 3^3}$$

$$= 2^{4-3} \times 3^{18-3} = 2 \times 3^{15}$$

LINKS

These are basic algebraic techniques which are used extensively in all the Pure and Applied Mathematics modules.

Pure Mathematics
- Logarithms and Exponentials (C2).
- Natural Logarithms and Exponentials (C3).
- Differentiation (C2).
- Integration (C2).
- Complex Numbers (FP2).

Test Yourself ▷L

1 Find the value of $(\frac{1}{3})^{-2}$.

   A -9 **B** $\frac{1}{9}$ **C** 9 **D** $-\frac{1}{9}$ **E** $-\frac{2}{3}$

2 Find the value of $\dfrac{36^{\frac{1}{2}}}{16^{\frac{3}{4}}}$, giving the answer in its simplest form.

   A $\frac{3}{4}$ **B** $\frac{3}{2}$ **C** $\left(\dfrac{36}{16}\right)^{-\frac{1}{4}}$ **D** 3 **E** $\frac{6}{8}$

3 Simplify $(2 - 2\sqrt{3})^2$, giving your answer in factorised form.

   A 16 **B** $8(2 - \sqrt{3})$ **C** $-8(1 + \sqrt{3})$ **D** $16 - 8\sqrt{3}$ **E** $4(4 - \sqrt{3})$

4 Simplify $\dfrac{(2x^4 y^2)^3}{10(x^3 \sqrt{y^5})^2}$.

   A $\frac{1}{5}x^6 y$ **B** $\frac{2}{25}x^6 y$ **C** $\dfrac{4x^6}{5y^4}$ **D** $\frac{4}{5}x^6 y$ **E** $\dfrac{8x^{12} y^6}{10x^6 y^5}$

5 Find the exact answer to $\sqrt{54 \times 48}$ simplifying your answer as much as possible.

   A 50.9 **B** $36\sqrt{2}$ **C** $12\sqrt{18}$ **D** 36 **E** $\sqrt{2592}$

Exam-Style Question ▷L

a) Find the value of $\left(\dfrac{16}{81}\right)^{\frac{3}{4}}$.

b) Simplify   i) $x^5 \div x^7$ ii) $\dfrac{3(a^5 bc^3)^2}{2a^6 b^4 c}$.

The language of mathematics

The language of mathematics and proof

A | ABOUT THIS TOPIC

This topic develops the problem-solving skills learned at GCSE and introduces the well defined language and symbols which are used in constructing a mathematical argument. It also presents some of the methods of proof (and disproof) that are widely used.

R | REMEMBER

Different types of numbers from GCSE.

K | KEY FACTS

Steps in solving a problem

1 Solve several similar but simplified problems.
2 Look for a pattern in your results.
3 Form a conjecture and make a prediction for more complicated cases.
4 Check your prediction.
5 Generalise your conjecture.

The modelling cycle (for real-life problems)

1 Make simplifying assumptions.
2 Define the variables and decide which techniques you need to use.
3 Represent the problem mathematically.
4 Solve the problem.
5 Check whether your solution is sensible; if not go back and review your simplifying assumptions.
6 Interpret the solution in the context of the original problem.

Types of numbers

Venn diagram showing the way in which the types of numbers are related to each other.

Natural numbers $\mathbb{N}$ (0, 1, 2, 3, ...)

Integers $\mathbb{Z}$ – the natural numbers and all the negative whole numbers (... −3, −2, −1, 0, 1, 2, 3, ...)

Rational numbers $\mathbb{Q}$ – all the integers and all the fractions $\left(\text{e.g.}\ \frac{2}{3}, -\frac{11}{5}\right)$

Real numbers $\mathbb{R}$ – all rational and irrational numbers (e.g. $\sqrt{2}, \pi$)

Writing mathematics

$P \Rightarrow Q$ This symbol means P **implies** Q or P **leads to** Q. P is a **sufficient** condition for Q.

$P \Leftarrow Q$ This symbol means P **is implied by** Q or P **follows from** Q. P is a **necessary** condition for Q.

$P \Leftrightarrow Q$ This symbol means P **implies and is implied by** Q or P **is equivalent to** Q. P is a **necessary and sufficient** condition for Q.

Mathematical statements

EXAMPLE 1	Say whether or not the following statements are correct.

i) The polygon is a quadrilateral $\Rightarrow$ The polygon is a square.
ii) The polygon is a quadrilateral $\Leftarrow$ The polygon is a square.
iii) The sum of the interior angles of a polygon is $360°$ $\Leftrightarrow$ The polygon is a quadrilateral.

SOLUTION	

i) This is not correct. A quadrilateral is any four-sided polygon, this does not imply that it is necessarily a square. For example, this parallelogram is a quadrilateral.

ii) This is correct. All squares have four sides so 'the polygon is a quadrilateral' follows from the statement the polygon is a square.

iii) This is correct. The sum of the interior angles of all four-sided shapes is $360°$ so the two statements are equivalent.

Converse of a theorem

The converse of $P \Rightarrow Q$ is $P \Leftarrow Q$.

EXAMPLE 2	A theorem states that 'For triangle ABC, $CA = CB \Rightarrow \angle A = \angle B$'. State the converse of the theorem.

SOLUTION	

If $\angle A = \angle B$, the two base angles of a triangle ABC are equal.
So the triangle is isosceles, i.e. $CA = CB \Leftarrow \angle A = \angle B$
which can be written as $\angle A = \angle B \Rightarrow CA = CB$.

Note Since this is the case, the theorem and its converse are both true, so you can use the symbol $\Leftrightarrow$:
$CA = CB \Leftrightarrow \angle A = \angle B$.
Notice that it is quite often the case that a theorem is true but its converse is false.

Proof in mathematics

A conjecture is a mathematical statement which appears likely to be true, but has not been formally proved to be true.

Making a conjecture or finding a formula that fits the results is not a proof. A proof shows that a conjecture is true for all cases, but it is sometimes easier to disprove a conjecture by finding a counter-example.

EXAMPLE 3

Disprove the conjecture that $n^2 + 1$ is a prime number for all n.

SOLUTION

If $n = 1$, $n^2 + 1 = 2$ which is prime
   $n = 2$, $n^2 + 1 = 5$ which is prime
   $n = 3$, $n^2 + 1 = 10$ which is NOT prime
There is a counter-example and so the conjecture is not true.

Proof by deduction

Start by stating a conjecture, then, starting from a known result or axiom, construct a logical argument as to why the conjecture must be true. This type of proof often uses algebra.

EXAMPLE 4

Prove the conjecture that the sum of two consecutive integers is always an odd number.

SOLUTION

It does not matter whether n is odd or even, the next number will always be $n + 1$ and will be odd if n is even and even if n is odd.

Step 1: Let the first integer be n then the second integer is $n + 1$.
Step 2: Add the integers $n + (n + 1) = 2n + 1$.
Step 3: Complete the argument: $2n$ is even since it is a multiple of 2
$\Rightarrow 2n + 1$ is odd since it is one more.
Hence the sum of two consecutive integers is always an odd number.

EXAMPLE 5

A panelled fence is built at the side of a terraced garden.
The first terrace has one fence panel.
Two more panels are added for the second terrace, giving three altogether.
Three more panels are added for the third terrace, giving six altogether.

i)   How many panels are needed for four terraces?
ii)   Find the relationship between t the number of terraces and p the number of fence panels.
iii) Show that your answer to part ii) works for a garden with six terraces.

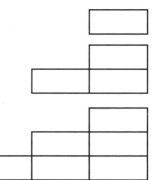

SOLUTION

i)

Number of terraces, t	1	2	3
Number of fence panels, p	1	3	6

First notice that there is a pattern in the way the fence panels are increasing. Use this to predict the number of panels for four terraces.

Number of terraces, t	1	2	3	4
Pattern	1	$1 + 2$	$1 + 2 + 3$	$1 + 2 + 3 + 4$
Number of fence panels, p	1	3	6	10

Ten fence panels are needed for four terraces.
This can be checked by drawing a diagram.

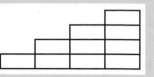

ii) By looking at the pattern, each time the answer is half of t multiplied by $t + 1$ so the conjecture is $p = \frac{1}{2}t(t + 1)$.

To prove this, think of putting two of each shape together to make a rectangle.
Its length is t and its height is $t + 1$.
It has $2p$ panels.
So $2p = t(t + 1)$
   $p = \frac{1}{2}t(t + 1)$

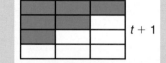

$t + 1$

iii) Using the formula with $t = 6$ gives $p = \frac{1}{2} \times 6 \times (6 + 1) = 3 \times 7 = 21$.

Note This result can also be checked by drawing the diagram for six terraces.

□ LINKS

These are fundamental techniques which are used extensively in Mathematics.

Test Yourself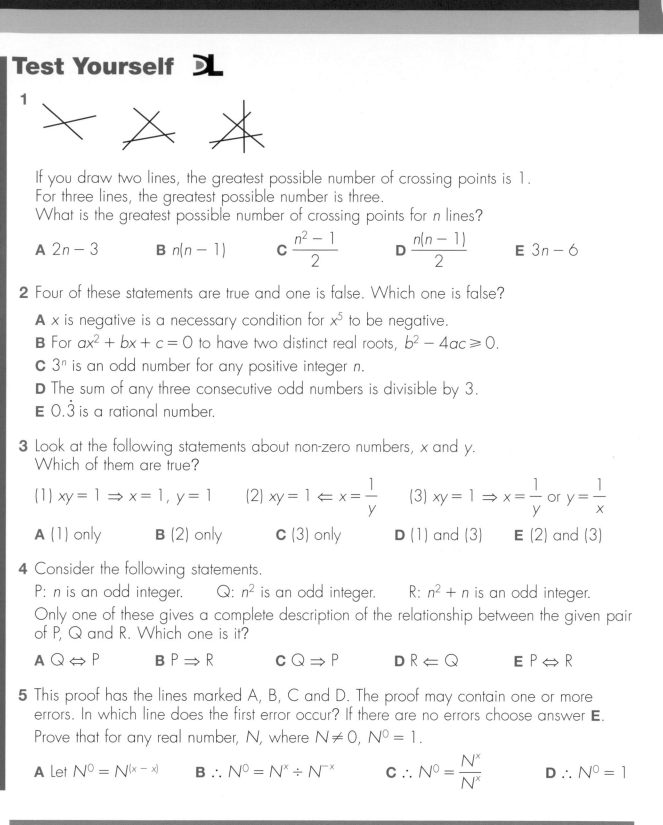

1

If you draw two lines, the greatest possible number of crossing points is 1.
For three lines, the greatest possible number is three.
What is the greatest possible number of crossing points for n lines?

A $2n - 3$ **B** $n(n - 1)$ **C** $\dfrac{n^2 - 1}{2}$ **D** $\dfrac{n(n - 1)}{2}$ **E** $3n - 6$

2 Four of these statements are true and one is false. Which one is false?

  A x is negative is a necessary condition for x^5 to be negative.
  B For $ax^2 + bx + c = 0$ to have two distinct real roots, $b^2 - 4ac \geqslant 0$.
  C 3^n is an odd number for any positive integer n.
  D The sum of any three consecutive odd numbers is divisible by 3.
  E $0.\dot{3}$ is a rational number.

3 Look at the following statements about non-zero numbers, x and y.
Which of them are true?

  (1) $xy = 1 \Rightarrow x = 1, y = 1$ (2) $xy = 1 \Leftarrow x = \dfrac{1}{y}$ (3) $xy = 1 \Rightarrow x = \dfrac{1}{y}$ or $y = \dfrac{1}{x}$

  A (1) only   **B** (2) only   **C** (3) only   **D** (1) and (3)   **E** (2) and (3)

4 Consider the following statements.
  P: n is an odd integer.   Q: n^2 is an odd integer.   R: $n^2 + n$ is an odd integer.
  Only one of these gives a complete description of the relationship between the given pair
  of P, Q and R. Which one is it?

  A $Q \Leftrightarrow P$ **B** $P \Rightarrow R$ **C** $Q \Rightarrow P$ **D** $R \Leftarrow Q$ **E** $P \Leftrightarrow R$

5 This proof has the lines marked A, B, C and D. The proof may contain one or more
errors. In which line does the first error occur? If there are no errors choose answer **E**.
Prove that for any real number, N, where $N \neq 0$, $N^0 = 1$.

  A Let $N^0 = N^{(x - x)}$ **B** $\therefore N^0 = N^x \div N^{-x}$ **C** $\therefore N^0 = \dfrac{N^x}{N^x}$ **D** $\therefore N^0 = 1$

Exam-Style Question

The smallest of five consecutive integers is n.
i)   Write down the next four integers in terms of n.
ii)   Prove that the sum of any five consecutive integers is divisible by 5.
iii)   Using your result from ii), write down the sum of 998, 999, 1000, 1001 and 1002.

INDEX

Formulae and results

Here are some formulae and results which you will need to recall or derive for the C1 examination. There is an underlying assumption that students already know all the results needed for GCSE Mathematics. The following list is not exhaustive, and you should check with your teacher before your examination.

Quadratic equations

The roots of the equation $ax^2 + bx + c = 0$ are $x = \dfrac{-b \pm \sqrt{b^2 - 4ac}}{2a}$.

The discriminant is $(b^2 - 4ac)$

Discriminant > 0: 2 real roots
Discriminant $= 0$: 1 repeated root
Discriminant < 0: No real roots

Modulus

$|x|$ means the positive value of x. For $x \geqslant 0$, $|x| = x$; for $x < 0$, $|x| = -x$.

$|x| < a \Leftrightarrow -a < x < a \quad (a > 0)$

Binomial coefficients

The notations ^nC_r and $\dbinom{n}{r}$ are equivalent.

$^nC_0 = {}^nC_n = 1$

Binomial coefficients may be found using Pascal's triangle:

$$
\begin{array}{ccccccccccc}
 & & & & & 1 & & & & & \\
 & & & & 1 & & 1 & & & & \\
 & & & 1 & & 2 & & 1 & & & \\
 & & 1 & & 3 & & 3 & & 1 & & \\
 & 1 & & 4 & & 6 & & 4 & & 1 & \\
1 & & 5 & & 10 & & 10 & & 5 & & 1
\end{array}
$$

and so on.

Indices

$a^m \times a^n = a^{m+n}$ 　　　 $a^m \div a^n = a^{m-n}$ 　　　 $a^0 = 1$

$a^{-m} = \dfrac{1}{a^m}$ 　　　 $a^{\frac{1}{n}} = \sqrt[n]{a}$ 　　　 $(a^m)^n = a^{mn}$

Straight lines

The line joining (x_1, y_1) to (x_2, y_2) has:

Gradient $\quad m = \dfrac{y_2 - y_1}{x_2 - x_1}$ $\qquad$ Length $\qquad \sqrt{(x_2 - x_1)^2 + (y_2 - y_1)^2}$

Equation $\quad \dfrac{y - y_1}{x - x_1} = \dfrac{y_2 - y_1}{x_2 - x_1}$ $\qquad$ Mid-point $\quad \left(\dfrac{x_1 + x_2}{2}, \dfrac{y_1 + y_2}{2} \right)$

Other formulae for the equation of a straight line:

Through $(0, c)$ with gradient m: $\qquad y = mx + c$

Through (x_1, y_1) with gradient m: $\qquad y - y_1 = m(x - x_1)$

Through $(a, 0)$ and $(0, b)$: $\qquad \dfrac{x}{a} + \dfrac{y}{b} = 1$

Perpendicular lines: the product of their gradients $m_1 m_2 = -1$.

Circles

The circle with centre (a, b), radius r has equation $(x - a)^2 + (y - b)^2 = r^2$.